THE GRADE CRICKETER

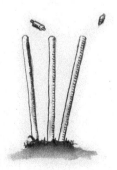

Published by Melbourne Books
Level 9, 100 Collins Street,
Melbourne, VIC 3000
Australia
www.melbournebooks.com.au
info@melbournebooks.com.au

National Library of Australia
Cataloguing-in-Publication entry
Authors: Sam Perry, Dave Edwards, Ian Higgins
Title: The Grade Cricketer
ISBN: 9781922129819 (paperback)
Cover Design: Julia Dowe
Subjects: Cricket--Australia--Humor.
Cricket stories.
Other Creators/Contributors:
Edwards, Dave J., Higgins, Ian A.
Dewey Number: A823.4

@GRADECRICKETER

THE GRADE CRICKETER

EDWARDS   PERRY   HIGGINS

M

MELBOURNE BOOKS

For all those who ever dreamed that
one day they'd play cricket for Australia.

CONTENTS

WHY DO I BOTHER?

I stand in front of the mirror in this bleak suburban dressing room. A weary-looking man stares blankly back at me. A man wearing long, grass-stained white pants, a baggy white shirt and a wide-brimmed cricket hat. A man whose face is lathered in sunscreen, flourishes of zinc covering his nose and cheeks. His shoulders are slumped; his eyes, once sparkling and alive, are now dead. This is a man collecting his thoughts ahead of yet another long, painful afternoon in the harsh Australian sun.

This is me. And this is what I've become.

I slowly pull away from the mirror and slink over to my usual corner position in the dressing room. As always, I scan the room to assess each of the 10 misfits with whom I've chosen to spend my weekend. Directly to my right is our brash, 22-year-old wicketkeeper, Timbo. Timbo has some of the worst chat I've ever had to endure. His hair is long and his hands are poor, but his confidence is something to be admired. Timbo wears a short-sleeved shirt, which is essentially his way of telling the batsman that he hasn't performed a stumping since

2007. This morning, when he entered the dressing room and put his cricket kit down next to mine, my heart instantly sank. I was hoping Nuggsy would get here first and claim his usual spot by my side, but if his text message at 4.25am is anything to go by — 'Where are you mate? We're kicking on to Lounge Bar! YIEW!' — he definitely had a massive night. In fact, it's nearly 1:30pm and he still hasn't turned up. Must have got a chop, in which case all is forgiven.

Next to Timbo is the new bloke. I don't actually know his name and hopefully I won't need to. I think it might be Darren, but I'll condescendingly refer to him as 'champ' until he proves himself. A quick glance at his kit reveals a luggage tag, which suggests that he's spent time playing in the UK. This could just be from a school cricket tour seven years ago, but I'm instantly intimidated, regardless. He has played cricket overseas and is therefore a threat to me.

One seat over from Timbo is Swampy. Swampy's a pretty solid bloke, but he's going through what seems like a painful divorce. Since Suzy walked out on him, Swampy has become increasingly prone to bursts of extreme fury. Last week, he absolutely destroyed the dressing room door after being given out caught behind when the ball flicked his thigh pad. The club has charged him $800 to fix the door, but Swampy's a bit low on cash now, so he's appealing the decision. On the upside, his drinking has increased four-fold since the separation, which means he's always good for post-match beers. He's usually knocked back seven before he gets out of the showers. Classic Swampy.

Wazza sits in the corner opposite me. He's definitely the best looking bloke in the team. I feel like he doesn't even know I exist, yet I know his batting average to the third decimal point. I'd really love to be mates with him one day; to bask in his reflected glory. I'd also love to know what hair product he uses, because whatever it is, it's working. Incredible volume.

John, who's sitting next to Wazza, is the smartest bloke I know. His cricket kit is impeccably maintained: pad straps all done up to keep their shape, bat placed inside its cover, training gear folded neatly away. I wish I had that kind of self-respect; my cricket kit looks like someone threw an IED in there. John's definitely a virgin, but he logs the scores into the online portal at the end of the day and he's handy with a crossword, so John's alright.

I briefly snap out of my malaise to catch a few words from our skipper, Robbo. 'Let's just fucking *work hard* and get these cunts out!' he implores us, for the fifteenth time this season. Robbo, all 5'8" of him, arches backwards to project his voice, the nasal tones echoing around the poorly insulated dressing room. Robbo is yet to put his pants on. I suspect this impassioned team talk might be more effective if he were actually wearing pants.

Robbo, a 39-year-old chartered accountant who still lives at home, turns up to every training session wearing a suit. I presume this is the only reason he was given the captaincy — the bloke set a 9-0 field last week for our part-time leg-spinner. Wearing a suit to training is an intelligent ploy when trying to establish political capital at any club. It indicates that other people think you are smart — or at the very least, have chosen to employ you. It's basic consumer confidence. In reality, Robbo had been unemployed for the best part of 14 months and was applying for interviews near the training ground.

Robbo's had many problems over the course of his life. I'd estimate he drinks 10-12 schooners after each game before driving home. No one ever thinks to stop him because he says some pretty funny things after about six or seven. Nothing funny after eight beers, though. I don't think he's ever paid his registration fees at the club, but I've seen him blow $400 on the pokies after training a couple of times. He also seems to have discovered ecstasy quite late in his life. He played first grade for half a season, though. I know this because he somehow manages to work it in to every conversation.

Bretty is our Chop King — and he's about as interested in the captain's fire-up talk as I am. I love it when Bretty asks me for a lift to the game because he'll always divulge, in sordid detail, his sexual escapades from the night before. For a bloke who works part-time at Target, Bretty's got a real knack with the ladies. I think he's slept with over 20 women this summer, which is significantly higher than his batting average, but that's mainly because I've never seen him play sober. It's fair to say that I live vicariously through Bretty. His chat is first class, his rig is excellent and his hair is something I've envied for a long time. He's got a great set of hands in the cordon too, which is funny because he never holds onto a girlfriend for more than 15 minutes. It's a shame my own catching is shit because I'd love to spend a day standing next to Bretty at second slip, feasting off his impossible sexual conquests and later retelling them as if they were my own.

Damo is the lucky bastard who's managed to burgle a spot next to Bretty. He's in his forties now and has played cricket for over 20 years, including a bit of first grade in the late 1990s. I'm not a psychologist, but I suspect that Damo's still playing because it's all he's ever known and he has a deep-seated fear of change. I think the bloke just needs other things in his life — a girlfriend or a hobby, at the very least — but he's the closest thing I've got to an idol so I'm pleased he's still around.

Sitting in the opposite corner are two private school kids, Nathan and Chris. They must be in the 4-6 percent body fat category; their skin folds are absolutely amazing. I too once boasted a rig of similar stature, back in the days when I could look at a dumbbell while eating a cheeseburger and still lose three kilograms. These kids have no idea how good they've got it.

Then, there's our scorer, Ronald. Ronald's a lovely bloke, but I sometimes wonder why he chooses to spend his Saturdays dutifully recording the fourth grade results with an HB pencil. I think it's because he hates his wife. Ronald's best known for passing around jelly-babies and snakes to keep our blood sugar levels up, which is still something I get ridiculously excited by. To summarise, Ronald's key function, for which he receives no remuneration, is to record our results and to ply us with jelly treats. He must really hate his wife.

Our home ground is located right next to a tennis club. Polite shouts of 'nice shot, Meryl' and 'I think that one hit the line, Albert!' can be heard from our dressing room; the sounds of seniors competing in friendly social games under beautiful blue skies. Meanwhile, we huddle together in this grim, indoor setting, as Bretty regales us with the filthy details of his latest seduction story.

At this point in my career, I'm clearly torn. I was once like Nathan and Chris, blessed with a ripping rig and a bright future. Now, I'm just a couple of years and a failed marriage away from being a Swampy or a Robbo. Once upon a time, I'd have breathed in every single word, every ounce of energy that our captain — our *leader* — would impart on us during the pre-game speech. Now, I'm wondering whether I should have gone a bit harder on the circuit last night. Wondering what it would be like to go to the beach on a Saturday for the first time since 1995. Pondering the pros and cons of this life that I have chosen for myself.

But deep down I still reckon I could play ones or twos anywhere else. Because inside every grade cricketer is a persistent voice telling you that a change of club is the answer. It doesn't matter that you haven't made a tangible contribution to any cricket team since you were 16. At a new club, you can start again.

I snap back into the present. Robbo is still talking. The way he's going, you'd think we were three wickets away from victory. I think he's forgotten we got bowled out before lunch.

Suddenly, I receive a text from Finn:

'Hey mate, is your game over yet? We're thinking of hitting up the beach this arvo...'

It's a gorgeous day outside. 29 degrees, faint breeze, not a cloud in the sky. My mates are heading to the beach, but I'm paying to play cricket against 11 terrible blokes who laughed when I got out.

'Sorry mate. We're just about to go out and defend 136,' I write back hastily.

I throw my phone back in the kit and allow myself a brief sigh. I tell myself I wouldn't want to be anywhere else, but the cold, hard reality of the situation sinks in. Sure, Nuggsy scored 730 runs last year and took 35 poles with a bowling average of 19.4, but my mates went to the beach twice so I'm not sure who had the better summer. The only woman at the ground today is Nathan's 59-year-old step-mum. I'm not even sure what a 'beach' is anymore; it's been years since I felt the sand between my toes.

Then, a knock on the door. It's the 74-year-old umpire with crippling arthritis in his knees. He wobbles into the dressing-room, face lacquered in 50+ sunscreen. 'We're on our way, lads.'

Fuck. Another Saturday. How did I get here?

1

I WAS GOOD

I used to be good at cricket.

As a kid, there was nothing better than the Saturday morning before a cricket match. Young, wide-eyed, and yet to encounter life's harsh realities, every Saturday felt like Christmas Day. I'd wake up, fresh-faced and clear-headed after 10 hours of uninterrupted sleep, ready to take on the world. The perfect state of mind to succeed in cricket. Fast-forward 20 or so years, and there's honestly nothing worse than the Saturday morning before a cricket match. Older, wearier, and now acutely aware of life's harsh realities, every Saturday feels like a fucking funeral. I wake up, sleep-deprived and bleary-eyed after a 10-hour post-work bender, ready to give up. The absolute worst state of mind to succeed in cricket.

As a kid, I was really quite a good cricketer, though. I can't prove it, obviously — this was a time before statistics were available for all to see online — but suffice to say that I was a bloody good player. I think my love of the game back then stemmed from my father. Dad was a surly type of very few words. He worked long hours at a complicated job that involved numbers and necessitated a leather briefcase, which he carried manfully with him everywhere he went. He always looked frustrated and weary, which perhaps gave the impression his job was more complicated than I'm giving him credit for. Perhaps, he just hated his life. During the week, Dad was a heavy yet almost invisible presence in the household. He'd arrive home late most nights, his loud footsteps marking the end of our brief *détente* period. He'd slink his weary 6'4" frame into the sofa; beer in one hand, remote in the other, glazed eyes staring blankly at the television. We knew he needed a good 20-30 minutes of time to himself, so we generously afforded him that. It was the least we could do.

As a kid, Dad refused to provide me with any overt affection or encouragement. It was a passive, unspoken refusal; sure, I could have sought his affection myself, but I feared his rejection. I still do. As such, I focused my energies on the cricket field — the one place where it seemed I had a chance to prove myself as a son. I was determined to gain my father's elusive love by scoring runs and taking wickets. It was the only way that the family could stay together.

On the odd occasion he finished work early, Dad would take me down to the nets. For hours, as day faded into dusk, he'd pepper me with throwdowns, sweating profusely, his shirt undone and tie askew, barking two-word commands at me: *'Elbow straight!' 'Work hard!' 'Head down!'* The lack of sex that Dad received during this period of his marriage was clearly integral to my career, in that he focused all his physical energy on giving me throwdowns. After my hit, of course, he'd demand that I bowl to him, where he would arrogantly dispatch my pre-teen bowling all over the park, perhaps living out a long-dormant fantasy of dominating a bowling attack once more. These foundations would serve me well for grade cricket in the future, in that I gained valuable experience bowling against a hard-nosed bastard who hated the shit out of me.

Soon enough, Dad entered me in the local club competition, where I effortlessly dominated my peers for several years. Having grown up facing my dad's frustrated medium-pacers, it was embarrassingly easy playing against a bunch of sheltered pin-dicks bowling 25 km/h with an *Incrediball* on synthetic pitches. It wasn't long before word got out — and soon enough, I was a 'representative cricketer.'

Rep cricket was where I really excelled. It was also where my unhealthy, lifelong obsession with 'kit' began. As you likely know, rep kit is a status symbol for young kids, regardless of the code. In the suburb where I grew up, no one incited more jealousy among his peers than the kid wearing representative rugby shorts. The club crest sitting handsomely on one side; the Canterbury logo on the other. It was 'official'; it was pure — and by god it was intimidating to the rest of us. When I received my rep kit for the first time, I truly felt like I'd made it. This apparel is reserved for a select few — and of course, I resolved to wear it at every given opportunity, regardless of the occasion or dress code requirement. I was now a 'rep cricketer' — and what's the point of being a rep cricketer if no one knows it? I needed every single person — from the 17-year-old female babysitter to the 67-year-old bloke serving me at IGA — to know that I had gained selection in a combined cricket team.

Eventually, I was given the captaincy, and, later, selected for even higher honours after one particularly productive season. While it wasn't a 'state' side *per se*, the combined team that I was selected for did include the name of my home state, and therefore, to my uneducated non-cricket mates, I *was* a state cricketer.

Of course, all this success had not escaped the attention of my father. Dad was driving me to every game, casting a watchful, judgemental eye over every innings I played, every ball I bowled. Even into my teens, my entire self-worth was based upon gaining approval from Dad. On match days, he'd let me sit in the front seat on the way home (if I had performed well). The chance to sit next to Dad on the return drive was what spurred me on at the crease; it was the catalyst for many of my underage triumphs. A personal milestone — say, a 50 not out, or a five-wicket haul — might even earn me the coveted double: a front seat position *and* Drive Thru McDonald's. I'd scoff down my Big Mac meal, a titanic wave of catharsis sweeping over me, all the while making sure not to drop a single crumb on the leather seat, lest I risk ruining this precious bonding moment. On the rare occasion that I did fail, it was the back seat for me, the gentle, fuzzy sound of ABC radio's *Grandstand* providing the aural backdrop for an otherwise silent homeward bound.

It wasn't just the desire to please my father that spurred me to such great heights as a child. I also wanted to get my name in the Sunday newspaper. All cricketers in the early-to-mid-1990s, prior to the widespread take-up of the internet, aspired to get their name in the paper. It's a sentiment that remains largely intact to this very day, despite the decline of print media and simultaneous emergence of online platforms such as MyCricket. I envisaged thousands of other youngsters trawling through the papers, as I did, squinting desperately in search for their own name amid the densely populated size four font. I hoped, tragically, that my 30-odd would be enough to make it, even though it was only the third-highest score of our innings. I genuinely craved public recognition of my talents. I was a tortured *artiste* with an enormous ego. Basically, I was the Kanye West of the U12 local cricket competition.

As I grew older, word of my on-field exploits grew stronger

— particularly at school. Here, I was seen as *the cricketer* — my entire identity hinged on the fact I was better than anyone else at a particular sport. It entitled me to a modicum of respect among the rugby-skewed 'jock' contingent: they understood that I was 'good' at a sport, even if it was one they didn't necessarily care much for, and I subsequently gained their moderate acceptance. Teachers, too, recognised that I was elite. Occasionally, I'd be permitted to leave class early to attend a rep training session. It goes without saying that these were the greatest days of my life. I am still known as *the cricketer* among former classmates, even all these years later. At a recent school reunion, I openly trumpeted my (vastly exaggerated) results at grade level — *'one level below state cricket, actually'* — and basked in the warm, familiar comfort that, at least among my school brethren, I was somebody. Obviously they can never know that I've averaged just 14.7 across all grades since graduation. Thankfully, no one asked about my career, marital status or investment portfolio during this brief jaunt down memory lane.

My greatest on-field achievement as a kid was the time I tonned up in an U16 representative game. Our opposition contained one future test player, rumoured to be bowling around 130+ *clicks* — even though he was about 14 at the time — so it was a big achievement. Throughout my glorious knock, I cleverly farmed the strike so as to avoid having to face the young paceman. My strategy was to peel a couple of boundaries off the part-time off-spinner and block the last ball of the over, thereby forcing my batting partner to fend off his frightening barrage of yorkers and bouncers. I'd stand at the non-strikers' end behind the umpire, refusing to back up, watching the wickets tumble. Today, I deliberately omit this act of cowardice when describing my chanceless knock at dinner parties and work functions.

I'll also neglect to mention the result (we lost in the last over, due to a bowling change error that I was responsible for).

This century was timely. The current state coach was in attendance; his kid, a wicketkeeper, was playing for the opposition. As I strolled arrogantly off the field, raising my bat to the crowd, I asked my teammates whether the coach had seen my innings. Perhaps he had been taking down notes, identifying me as a Sheffield Shield prospect; making a few phone calls to national selectors to get me on a plane for the U17 World Cup? Maybe, just maybe, this was my big break?

'Actually, he slept through the entire thing,' one of my mates informed me, with obvious relish.

I was crestfallen. Obviously, my 137 (not out) off 146 deliveries lacked the entertainment value required to keep this bloke from falling unconscious. At the same time, I felt sorry for his son. His Dad would rather catch a few zeds than watch him play cricket. Alpha'd by your own dad. Fuck me.

Having dominated the junior circuit for 5-6 years, my cricket career looked promising. However, I was coming towards what many describe as the 'crossroads' — where I would be forced to choose between cricket and study. While I wanted to 'play cricket for Australia', there was an overwhelming expectation from my parents — particularly Mum — to get a good entry mark to university. It is no surprise that during these critical late-high school years, my cricket suffered tremendously. As it turned out, I never ended up playing cricket for Australia, nor did I attend university, so I bet my parents are really proud of the man I have become.

To be honest, high school cricket felt pointless by the time I reached Year 12. I'd been in the school's first XI since the age of 14, tapped early as the youngster of the future, stoically facing up against near-adults with all the confidence in the world. But three years later, in my final academic year, the novelty had worn off. I was an elder statesman at 17, playing against pubescent children. My sledging became increasingly aggressive and profane. My batting suffered; my captaincy was questionable. It was a telling snapshot into the future. School was about to end, and I was about to be thrust out into the real world, where high-school cricket stats mean nothing.

Nothing will ever compare to that brief period in time when I was great. From the age of 10-17, I had the cricketing world on a string. My batting average was excellent; my bowling action was pure; my teenage rig required very little upkeep. Nowadays, my batting average is lower than Bretty's iPhone battery after a full day of Tinder. On the rare occasion I'm called upon to bowl, my ungainly action draws an audible gasp of horror from the batsman. And my rig? Let's just say that I'm in no danger of earning a rig-based call-up to second grade.

I'm 99 percent sure that this will be my last season.

When I was about 10 or 11, my parents — having duly recognised my burgeoning, undeniable talent — decided to buy me a cricket bat for Christmas. I woke up that morning to see a suspiciously shaped present nestled under the tree. I quickly tore the wrapping off, eyes ablaze, literally salivating at the prospect of owning an actual cricket bat.

My first bat was a size six blade crafted from Kashmir Willow, which sounded exotic at the time. I was quietly impressed that despite being caught in an at-times violent territorial dispute between India and Pakistan, the Kashmiri people were still able to establish such a thriving industry, but equally saddened that this was the likely reason for the decades-long conflict. Every week or so, Dad and I would coat the bat with linseed oil, leave it to dry for about a day, then carefully sandpaper it back to achieve a smooth finish. Dad was particularly invested in the maintenance of this bat. At times, it felt like he cared for it more than me. At times, he may well have. Regardless, breathing in the strong, pungent fumes from the linseed oil; running my 10-year-old fingers over the various 'grit' levels of the sandpaper, savouring its coarseness — I felt like a man for the very first time. It was masculinity in its purest form: a father and son bonding over a cricket bat purchased at Rebel Sport.

The make of the bat was a Slazenger V100 — a hat tip to Mark Waugh, my cricketing idol. The primary redness of the 'V' popped off the blade; the '100' implied that centuries were on the horizon. It was the perfect first bat for a young aspirational cricketer who dared to dream. I of course aimed to emulate Mark Waugh in every facet of my life. His casual, stylish swagger became a trademark of mine even as a kid; my efforts to elegantly whip everything off my pads would at times bring me undone, but I always *looked good*. Looking good was — and remains — the most important part of being a cricketer.

Soon enough, like a married man with an increasingly wandering eye, I began to take an active interest in other people's bats. A lot of my teammates came from 'privileged' backgrounds. This was reflected in the proliferation of quality bats that emerged out of the woodwork, quite literally, during the early stages of my rep career. Almost overnight, I found myself bowling to players with test-quality English willow, when just weeks earlier the playing field was level. Christmas 1997 was a fruitful period for the bat industry, it seemed.

One teammate, who came from a particularly high socioeconomic background, had recently been gifted the Gunn & Moore *Diamond* cricket bat, drawing considerable envy upon unveiling it for the first time at training. The sheer modernity of the blade, with its refreshing blue-green colour palate and angular diamond-shaped cut, intrigued me. It looked like it was from the future. This was the direction that bats were going, I realised. Suddenly, my V100 didn't seem so hot.

We were entering an arms race — and I needed to bolster my artillery. My first bat got the job done, but my second bat had to be a statement. I wanted to inspire jealousy at training, just as my teammate had done. I wanted it to be of the highest-grade English willow, with 6-8 perfectly spaced grains on the blade. I wanted kids to know how much it cost (which they would, of course, because we were all very familiar with the Queensgrove catalogue, even at that age). And just for that extra little edge, I wanted a bat cover, too; a holster to draw my weapon from, like a medieval swordsman.

As a kid, I spent a lot of time browsing the Queensgrove catalogue. However, I had yet to actually visit this mythical, much-vaunted Mecca. I had heard plenty about it from my teammates, though, who spoke with wide-eyed enthusiasm about this wondrous sporting complex. It sounded vast, plentiful, like Willy Wonka's Chocolate Factory, but for cricketers.

I had to make this pilgrimage; I had to.

I took the train out there to do my initial reconnaissance. The journey took over an hour, taking me out to some strange foreign outpost that, to my young eyes, resembled an industrial wasteland, or some shit. I hopped off the train and strolled over to the famed warehouse, trembling at the thought of what lay ahead. A rush of nervous energy permeated my tiny 12-year-old body: I was about to look at cricket bats.

The shop attendant couldn't have been much older than 22 and freckle-faced, his skin frighteningly raw and sunburnt. Having caught my eye, he offered me a benevolent yet odd greeting, where one half of his mouth formed a smile and the other half lay completely motionless — as if he could only be bothered to complete half the job. For that brief moment, he resembled a stroke victim. He was wearing a slightly-too-tight Queensgrove polo, with the sleeves rolled up to accentuate his (newly acquired) pipes. I assumed, safely, that he played something called 'grade'. I was not yet sure of what 'grade cricket' meant, but I understood it to be competitive, elite, and played by intelligent, consenting adults.

'What can I help you with, *champ*?' the young man asked me, nonchalantly.

Having not heard this word before, and quite startled by the aggressive upward inflection, I paused briefly before answering: 'I need a good cricket bat so I can *look good*.'

I told him that the bat needed to be expensive but affordable enough that Dad wouldn't completely lose his shit. It also needed to be *buzzworthy*, new to the market place and manufactured using the latest technological advances in bat making. I stressed that this bat would be seriously integral to my social standing over the short-term, and that I viewed this investment as a chance to establish my personal brand as a cricketer.

Slightly taken aback by my candour, the Queensgrove attendant nonetheless computed the brief. 'No dramas, *champ*. We'll sort you out. Come with me.'

Again with the 'champ'! What was this strange new word, and why did it make me feel slightly inferior? I bottled my emotions and followed his lead.

We started by browsing the Grey Nicolls section, then shuffled across to Kookaburra, Millichamp & Hall and several other notable brands. Throughout, the young attendant pointed out the bats specific to international cricketers. Mark Taylor's Stuart Surridge *Turbo*. Michael Slater's Grey Nicolls *Millennium*. Steve Waugh's GM *Maestro*. They seemed even more beautiful in the flesh. One particular bat in the Gunn & Moore section caught my eye: The GM *Purist*. The word *Purist* appealed to me instantly. Webster's defines 'purist' as 'a person who insists on absolute adherence to traditional rules or structures, especially in language or style.' Even at this young age, I knew that coaches generally frowned upon anything outside the norm. The *Purist* was more than a bat; it was an ethos, a belief system. It would subsequently form the basis of my entire approach to cricket. Now, I needed to sell it to my Dad and make this dream a reality.

In his book, *In Search of the Lost Grail of Middle Management: The Renaissance of Middle Managers,* Quentin R. Skrabec describes the prime years for a middle manager as 30 to 45. *At 45 you should be prepared, if necessary, to start an alternative career,* he writes. At this stage of his career, Dad was a depressed, anxious, cash-poor 52-year-old man who worked in middle management. His corporate ambition — once burning brightly — had since simmered to a standstill. Occasionally, he'd have enough disposable income to take us on a week long family holiday to some (usually tropical) location, where we would get a bit of sun before returning to our uninspiring suburban lives, perhaps hating each other slightly more for the experience. But in the main, money was tight.

But this bat was important, with the implications far-ranging. I

with a proposal. I told him that my peers — streets
...tural ability — were now using expensive, top-of-
bats. These bats offered them a clear advantage over
me, and I was concerned it could jeopardise my future selection
in representative teams. I also told him that my self-esteem would
suffer irreparably if I were *forced* to continue using a $60 bat. Having
listened patiently to my sales pitch, Dad agreed to accompany me to
Queensgrove. It was at that moment I knew I had him — and the GM
Purist — in the bag. Sure enough, Dad forked over the money and
suddenly, I was the proud sole owner of a top-line cricket bat.

Backyard cricket was a huge part of my life — as it is for any young
Australian, regardless of gender, who harbours an ambition to play
cricket for their country. The backyard was my fortress. The house
belonged to my parents, but the backyard, well, that was mine. My
mother's efforts to maintain a once-thriving garden were in vain; I
fucking owned that patch of land.

The backyard itself was quite traditional: a large stretch of grass
backed on to the house, with a plain wooden fence surrounding the
yard. A kidney-shaped swimming pool was positioned, effectively,
at 'long mid-off,' and would result in 'six and out' for the particularly
daring batsman. The pool's primary function was to act as a deterrent
for audacious stroke-play, so rarely was it used for actual swimming.
Much to my mother's displeasure, the grass — once a healthy, evenly
mowed green — had swiftly eroded to resemble a dusty, barren desert.
The bowlers' footmarks had created potholes, which would morph
into mud puddles after a bit of rain. The flowerbed — unfortunately

stationed at extra-cover — copped an absolute beating, left withered and lifeless, the unwitting victim of a cricketing genocide. Eventually, my mother gave up trying to maintain the garden. My love for backyard cricket probably shaved about $50,000 off the value of the property.

My brother, two years my junior, never really expressed a great interest in cricket growing up. He was, however, *two years my junior*, and thus served as my human backyard bowling machine throughout his entire childhood. He was academically gifted, my brother. While this was often a source of friction between us, it did allow me to position myself as the family 'athlete'. I was the sportsman; he was the scholar. He had the brains, granted, but what did that really mean at the age of 14? Sure, the future looked rosy for him — career, money, property, relationships, family — but that was *years* away. I had a good rig and an exquisite cover drive — and I had it *now*. To be fair, I'm certain he derived *some* enjoyment from bowling to me for hours on end. If nothing else, it certainly hardened him up. In my defence, I was only doing what my dad did to me: dominate him relentlessly in a bid to feel good about myself. Anyway, I'm pretty sure my childhood bullying helped give him the courage to launch his own start-up company earlier this year (which has already garnered significant interest from several US-based venture capitalists), so he probably owes me one. He actually called me the other day to tell me he's buying a new harbour-side apartment. Meanwhile, I'm paying my grade cricket registration fees this season in nine instalments.

Whenever he wasn't around to feed my insatiable desire for backyard cricket, I would invite my cricket-minded friends over to partake in a test match or two. As the host, I was already familiar with all the intricacies of the pitch. I knew that it was particularly conducive to off-spin, duly helped by the natural gradient of the land. I was also aware that the ball kept very low when pitched full of a length — a direct result of using my feet to my brother's terrible leg-spinners, an act which had rendered that patch of grass utterly barren. I scored a lot of centuries on that pitch. And whenever there was no one available to bowl to me, I'd improvise. They say that Bradman honed his craft by hitting a golf ball with a stump against a wall, or some shit. Well, that method seemed a bit antiquated for me — not to mention loud and potentially dangerous — so I settled for a plastic bat and a tennis ball. The trick was to throw the ball against the wall and quickly get into position to face the rebound. Not a lot to it, in retrospect, but I loved it. I'd dream up real-life cricketing scenarios, which almost always involved Australia chasing a daunting total. I was the young debutant tasked with saving a crucial test match after a top-order collapse. I'd be up against the West Indies, with Curtly Ambrose and Courtney Walsh the sworn enemy. They were scary, tall, dark, villainous; I was the young kid called upon to negotiate their unrelenting barrage of hostile short-pitched bowling. I'd assemble different pieces of outdoor furniture around me to simulate close-in fielders. It was good versus evil — and I was always *good*.

This type of role-play would last all the way until dinner. While my mates were out socialising after school — going on nervous dates with girls, losing their virginity — I was at home, by myself, hitting a tennis ball against a wall. Not that I envied them; in fact, I was deathly afraid of girls. I had no idea how to converse with them due to the fact that, generally speaking, they were not interested in things like batting averages. I dreamt of one day meeting a girl that liked cricket. Mainly, I just wanted somebody to give me throwdowns.

2

A DECADE OF GRADE CRICKET

I've now played 10 seasons of grade cricket. That equates to around 150 matches, over 200 weekends, complemented by 400 training sessions, and enough financial investment to sufficiently cripple my ability to purchase property for at least a decade.

My first few years of grade cricket were pivotal in shaping the man I am today. I've already described how good I was as a junior cricketer, so my reputation preceded me when I entered the titillating world of men's cricket. When I joined our club, I felt like a star. As a prodigy, this was nothing new to me. At my first 'selection night', our club secretary touted me as a 'player of promise.' His assessment carried great personal weight for me at age 17; in fact it still does — maybe even more so now. That I later learnt he was a prolific philanderer with an embezzlement conviction and a penchant for Asian prostitutes was immaterial. His credibility was, and is, safe with me. I rode this assessment and I rode it hard. I am a player of promise, I would say to myself. *I am a player of promise.* In the early 2000s, no family function passed without me pivoting to our club secretary's comment. It rang through my ears and rolled off my tongue sumptuously.

But then grade cricket got hard. Gone were the regular appearances in the paper that I'd become so accustomed to as a junior. My on-field performance degenerated into an exercise in naked mediocrity, which shook me to my very core. And this was only half the problem. If my on-field performances were bad, my off-field reputation was worse. I could accept that the majestic 30s and 50s of my youth had now been replaced with grisly 13s and 23s; I came to terms with the fact that I was no longer 'rapid' with the ball. It was away from the sanctuary of the cricket field that I was most vulnerable. There existed a world of intangible social rules, and as a naïve 17-year-old I was found wanting.

It started with one word. It seemed that everywhere I went, whether on the pitch or away from it, I heard the faint echo of one expression: 'Yuck.'

When I started at my first club, three weeks passed without anybody speaking to me. I was devastated. Sure, I knew one or two guys my age from juniors, but I considered myself on a different level, so I avoided any association with them. But while no one spoke to me directly, I did feel as though people were speaking *about* me, and that's where I came across this confounding term.

For reasons still unknown to me, a guy called 'Nuggsy' approached me during training, offering a confident 'G'day', muttering something obscure about being 'the Nuggler'. I should say his introduction wasn't the warmest: his handshake was hard and alarmingly masculine. He was also looking over my shoulder mid-shake. I needed someone to talk to me, though, so I accepted his cold introduction with a full heart and damp eyes. He was difficult to read back then, Nuggsy. He had a disturbing emotionlessness to him. Nevertheless he *had* spoken to me, so I felt a degree of safety.

I had one burning question, so I went for it.

'Mate, what is "yuck"?' I half-whispered, trembling.

He looked at me with dead eyes, his mind clearly ticking over the implications of my enquiry. He had approached me, and I had responded with insecurity. He had just met me. He was uncomfortable. Yet he must have seen an opportunity, because his eyes narrowed, his mouth curled into this makeshift, crooked half smile — *that stroke smile again! The same as that guy from Queensgrove!* — and there he stood poised to change my life forever.

'Your rig, mate. It's your rig. It's very sloppy.'

I was aghast. I didn't understand what Nuggsy meant, specifically, but I had learnt something more important. Whatever a 'rig' was, I never wanted it to be called 'yuck'.

Nuggsy's comment hurt me deeply, but his honesty was nonetheless refreshing. What's more, he was the first person to speak to me in weeks. This was a bloke who had been around for while. A bloke who had the 'ear' of the selection panel. A bloke who was never, under any circumstances, 'champed' by first graders. I needed to know his secrets to success in grade cricket. I needed to grasp this opportunity now.

'Want to grab a beer after training?' I blurted.

Having successfully lured Nuggsy over to the local pub with the promise of a beer, I was determined to make the most of our time together. This was a bloke who oozed everything grade cricket. What's more, he seemed surprisingly compassionate towards my plight. Perhaps he, too, had experienced a rocky start to his grade cricket experience. I told Nuggsy that despite my great efforts at training, I wasn't getting anywhere. No one knew who I was. I was just another kid with a mediocre rig filling up the numbers in the lower grades, destined for a career average of 13.8.

'Mate, I've only been here for a few weeks, but I don't think anyone even knows my name. I've already slipped three spots down the batting order. I've got no idea what the lyrics to the club song are. And every time I get a hit at training, I hear the faint sound of blokes whispering that one word under their breath: "Yuck." What am I doing wrong?' I began, nervously.

Nuggsy paused, took a long swig of his Reschs schooner, and reclined languidly into his seat. He scratched his bald head for a moment, seemingly in deep thought, before embarking on the long-winded response that would indeed shape my cricketing future. 'Listen, bud. You're a *grade* cricketer now. And it's time you learned a little bit about what that means. This isn't club cricket, "Shires" cricket, or that stupid school shit that you wasted your time on for all those years. This is *grade cricket*: the highest level of amateur cricket in the world,' he said with pride.

Just for those who don't already know, I should quickly provide a bit of background on the grade cricket competition. Grade cricket (or 'Premier cricket', as it is known in some states/territories) is the level directly below the state competition. Despite this close proximity to the professional arena, it is nonetheless an amateur competition. Sure, one or two first graders might get paid a little bit under the table, but everyone else must pay a registration fee in order to play. Normally, each club has four to five grades — first grade being the strongest; fifth grade the weakest. Those in first grade enjoy a status that the fifth graders can only dream about. Being a first grader is like being a celebrity to 50 blokes whose names you'll never know — or never even *need* to know — unless you end up playing with them after a severe run of poor form (or a serious disciplinary breach). The rest of the club — seconds, thirds, and fourth grade — is basically an assortment of talented youngsters and ageing desperates. The common denominator between the young and old brigade is that they were all once told they were 'good enough to play for Australia'. In many cases, it was the first and last compliment they ever received — and the reason why they're still playing. In all cases, it was the worst thing that could have ever happened to them. The ultimate grade cricketer, therefore, will possess the perfect balance of *good* and *not good enough* that will haunt them for all of their playing days. All this of course, is something that can only be learned with experience. At this early stage in my grade cricket career, I considered these young players to be 'cool' and the older players worthy of my respect.

Nuggsy tilted his head to one side as he lit up a cigarette. He took a deep drag, holding it in for what seemed like hours, before launching his head back to expel a thick plume of smoke towards the ceiling. 'Listen, *great* man,' he began. 'Success in grade cricket has nothing to do with skill, ability, or even results. It's all about the social ladder, bud. You've got the big dogs up top, the peasants down the bottom, and everyone in between is just trying to stay relevant,' he offered.

In many ways, grade cricket social hierarchy bears great similarity to the feudal systems that first appeared in the Middle Ages in Europe — something I'd learned a bit about at high school. As I remembered, kings and monarchs sat at the top, enjoying their pick of the land, women and food. They were the ones who established the rules that everyone had to live under. The barons leased their land from the king; the knights leased their land from the barons; and the knights granted the lowly peasants their land. The peasants were not allowed to marry, nor could they even leave the manor without permission. Basically, they were the fifth graders of the 8-12th Century.

'Mate, *I* want to be a big dog one day. How do I go about making that happen?' I asked.

Nuggsy sat up in his seat and looked me straight in the eye. 'Don't worry too much about runs, *big guy*. That's your first mistake. When we met, I told you your rig was sloppy, didn't I? Well it is. That's the first thing you've got to sort out.'

This was my 'oh, shit' moment. The rig, in case you've been living under a rock, is the male body. Specifically the torso, but not always. Looking good naked is absolutely imperative if you want to be taken seriously as a grade cricketer. Most of us are time poor these days, so there's really no point training anything beneath your lower abdominals. You wear long white pants during the game, anyway. Two muscle groups are crucial: chest and pipes. If you've got decent pipes, your shirt will tightly hug your torso and give others the impression you are strong. It might even get you first in line for a promotion up the order if some big hitting is required.

In the melting pot of grade cricket, your rig says more about you than your runs. A good rig offers tangible and intangible freedoms that sloppy rigs don't enjoy. It affords you freedom from oppression in the dressing room, specifically the freedom to shower free of harassment. It affords you freedom of expression with regards to training kit. While Skins are the sole reserve of those in second grade or higher, a training singlet is the exclusive domain of strong rigs, regardless of grade. At the end of my first season I vowed that I wouldn't return unless I was able to pull off a training singlet. In retrospect, if it weren't for those winter months of split sets and supplements, my life would have taken a different course. A good rig also offers you freedom of speech. While there are notable exceptions, those players enslaved to the title of 'shit rig' rarely enjoy good careers. They will be subjected to cruel and degrading treatment, and rightfully so. Why? Because they've got a shit rig.

But mainly, a good rig affords you freedom from the word 'yuck'.

Grade cricket compelled me to look at my rig square in the eye. It's decent enough now, but of course I can't be sure. I'm not ridiculed like I once was, but I'm no Bretty, either. I used to have pretty good hair, but it's decidedly thinning. I've focused heavily on my arms and chest, though I wish they were better. They could always be better. Bretty has always led the way in the domain of chest and arms, and I'd easily substitute 1000 career runs for his bicep girth. Maybe even 2000, if I had that many to give.

My stomach is a weird shape and it's always bothered me. I can get those little line thingy's that separate your abs from your pelvis, but never much definition in the actual abs. My belly button has an ungainly protrusion, so I always make sure my towel covers it. This means my towel sits fractionally higher around my waist than what is considered normal, so it's a point of anxiety for me. I've also never been the biggest fan of my general body shape; when I stand side-on, my back has an unattractive curvature that accentuates any stomach fat I'm carrying. Yuck, indeed. Despite a zillion squats a week, I never seem to lose anything off my buttocks, either. I used to do a mountain of cardio until I realised it did nothing for my rig. These were wasted years. Years I could have spent building my biceps. And chest.

Nuggsy continued on. 'Seriously, *legend*. A bloke might have a six-figure salary at a job he truly loves, but it all means nothing if he has a shit rig and a poor grasp of *Anchorman* quotes. It probably doesn't even matter if he averages in the mid-30s and does a lot at the club, because he'll never go anywhere.'

I briefly wondered as to the relevance of Will Ferrell movie quotes, but then remembered back to my first training session. I had overheard a crew of second graders reciting dialogue from the movie *Step Brothers* while mucking around on the slips cradle. Obviously this broad style of comedy had particular resonance within grade cricket circles. The humour was absurd, male-skewed, anti-intellectual, and highly quotable. Suddenly, I was beginning to understand the things that made grade cricketers tick. Meanwhile, Nuggsy continued to bluster on, flecks of spit now hissing out from his animated mouth. The next piece of advice he had for me revolved around women: a subject I knew little about.

Dad had never spoken to me about sex before. The only time we'd come close was when we were both up late one night after a One Day match between England and Australia, when I was about 10 years old. Dad flicked over to SBS and there was some raunchy Spanish movie on, with the main characters smack bang in the middle of a simulated sex scene. I remember everything: the heaving bosom, the cries of ecstasy, the incongruous Latin jazz soundtrack. Dad and I watched the entire scene in complete silence. At one point, I looked over to him, hoping he would switch the TV off and end this awkward moment, only to see he had a strange smirk on his face, his eyes glued to the set. He was not about to inform me that this was a beautiful, consensual act between a man and a woman who were in love. He needed this.

So it fell to Nuggsy, a 31-year-old bachelor who lived with his Mum, to tell me about sex. 'It's a numbers game, pure and simple,' he chuckled. 'You know that bloke, Stewey, in fifth grade? He's got a gorgeous wife and three beautiful children, but so what? No one wants to hear about little Madeline's finger-painting at Kindergarten, or how Susan manages to juggle raising the kids with her job as a barrister. However, if you're a second grader who's slept with three birds in the past month, you're a club hero. If you're a moderately good cricketer who can tell an engaging sex story, you are instantly among the upper echelon of the social ladder. Now don't get me wrong: having a girlfriend is a wonderful thing. But for God's sakes, don't ever bring her to a game — unless you enjoy the prospect of 10 blokes speculating over your sex life all day. That said, if you are comfortable disclosing these graphic details, you'll win a great deal of respect among your teammates.'

'So basically what you're saying is that I should work on my rig, get my chat right, sleep with some random women, and everything will go from there?' I ventured.

'That'll help a lot, *pal*, absolutely. But don't forget that cricket is a sport largely made up of individual battles between you and your teammates. As such, I strongly advise that you keep a close eye on the weekly performances of your teammates — and those at the club in general. When chatting to someone at training, only ask how well he performed on the weekend when you've already received prior confirmation of his failure. That might sound sociopathic, but believe me, the last thing you want is to turn up to training on Tuesday to hear, to your surprise, that a bloke in the grade below you tonned up.'

I frantically scribbled Nuggsy's advice down on a notepad. It was probably somewhat unbecoming to be taking notes, but this was valuable information.

'But you're good enough to succeed in grade cricket, bud,' he continued, earnestly. 'I knew it the first day I saw you in the nets. You remind me a lot of myself — and I'm going to help you get up the grades where you belong. Now do you reckon you can spot me another beer? My pay cheque doesn't come through until tomorrow.'

The chat with Nuggsy had gone well. I realised that he was taking me under his wing. I was now his *protégé* — and I looked forward to deploying these strategies in the coming months. It had been a slow start to my grade cricketing career, but with the help of Nuggsy, I felt like I could really make it. I had hope.

'A jug of Reschs, thanks *champ*,' I instructed the barman, with newfound confidence.

Everything made sense after Nuggsy's little chat with me. It was clear that the grade cricket political system was feudal and I was a leper. Nuggsy showed me that I had to cure this disease and it wasn't going to be through runs or wickets — though they can help — it was going to be through a tight rig and good chat. And so for the first three or four years of my grade cricket life I focused on just that. I lifted and I circuited. I did cardio in pre-season, which had nil positive effect on my cricket results but allowed me to see the boys and exchange sex stories. I ruthlessly watched popular Will Ferrell offerings and immersed myself in the dialogue for later quoting. And guess what, soon enough, things changed. I graduated from the 'third net' — usually reserved for other cricketing lepers who sometimes wear whites to training — to the middle net.

As far as on-field results go, for 10 years I've been what most would describe as middling to poor. As I've matured, I've come to understand the diminishing relationship between on-field results and selection in higher grades, but nevertheless I will provide a brief profile. I am a batsman, and I have settled for a serviceable batting average of somewhere between 13.5 and 18 in every single season I've played. In terms of playing style, it's pretty simple: if it's full, I'll drive. If it's short, I'll pull aggressively. If it's anywhere in between, I'm fucked. In the rare event I make two 30s in a row, I will move up a grade. On those occasions I will bat 8 and not bowl. As a result I assume the role of political attack dog in the field. Harsh, personal sledging is my forte and I don't resile from these obligations. In fact I enjoy them more than the game itself. There's nothing that makes me feel more alive than sledging a 15-year-old all day before getting into my 1991 Nissan Pulsar and driving to my parents house. Absolutely nothing.

Like many, I haven't totally abandoned the idea that I will one day become a professional cricketer. And if I'm not dreaming about playing first grade, or gaining selection as an overage player in the newly formed Futures League, I'm dreaming about the coveted 'triple C': the Century, Circuit, Chop. To score a hundred during the day, get drunk with your mates all night, and then have sex with a woman later that evening — all within a 12-hour period — is to achieve the holy trinity of amateur sport. If I am honest, it's the slim chance of nailing this mouth-watering trifecta that drives me to continue playing cricket. I have never done it, not yet, but I desperately want to.

As you can see, grade cricket is a twisted and backward thinking society. The more I see it, immerse myself and revel in it, the more I realise its absurdities. But it's all I've known. I've often read how heroin users continually chase that first high. I've never done heroin because it's the wrong kind of drug to be taking if you're to be accepted amongst your teammates. In many ways, however, grade cricket is my heroin. I sort of know that I'm past all of this now and that my world is so full of unreached potential, but I think about that one perfect cover drive I hit at training four weeks ago and it fills me with this warmth. I feel like I could still be good enough to play first grade. It crawls into my bloodstream and I feel whole again.

That's why I play cricket.

3

I HAVE MATES OUTSIDE CRICKET

Should you mix cricket with the rest of your life? Most grade cricketers would say no. The decision to mix your cricket and non-cricket friends can result in a horrible aftertaste. In all my time as a player, I have *never* seen the two groups mix successfully. Integrated, maybe. Assimilated, maybe. But not ingrained. However, there have been moments where I've succumbed to ambition and entertained the thought that maybe, just maybe, both groups could get along. I've sadly learnt the hard way. More on that later.

Finn is my best friend outside of cricket. We have been near-best mates for twenty years, going through school together as children, teenagers, and into adulthood. He was there for the formative years: the first cigarette, the high school parties, female liaisons and penis insecurities. Finn is a musician — a singer. He was in all sorts of choirs and singing groups at school. Before puberty he had a beautiful falsetto voice, and I gather that he managed his transition to adolescence with distinction. I never really appreciated his talent in school; as 'the cricketer' I distanced myself from anything that had the potential to detract from my masculinity. Singing was 'gay', and I didn't want to go near it.

Privately, I really liked music, and Finn knew it. I often found myself singing at home when no one was around. Finn overheard me one day as he entered the house, but to his credit, he was cool with it; even encouraged me. Because that was Finn — open, accepting, encouraging. Before long, he was harmonising my melodies, and for the first time, I felt the joy of playing music from the heart. He must've always known I was interested in music, because it didn't seem to bother him at all that I — 'the sportsman' — shared his passion. It was like he already knew. Although I'd always trusted him, I swore him to secrecy by physically threatening him if word got out. He hasn't told a soul, and we continue to sing together, in private, whenever we get a chance. He's a great friend.

Finn has been clear that he has no interest in cricket. Sure, he might keep an eye on a couple of the international fixtures — 'this looks much more athletic than the stuff I've seen you play,' he'd say — but that's about it. He has zero interest in conversation about rigs, and doesn't lift at all. Interestingly, it has no impact on his ability to engage in either short sexual trysts or long-term relationships. He has no chest or biceps to speak of, but he's pretty slim and his clothes look good on him. His diet's OK, I guess, so good luck to him.

Finn has a long-term band and a couple of other projects on the side. He's the front man for all of them and has made a bit of money from it, too. I like to give Finn advice on performance and team building, mainly because I think grade cricket is more 'elite' than his pursuit. In reality, I'm just regurgitating one-liners from pre-season sessions about culture. I monitor his performance when I'm watching him play a gig because I, too, know what it's like to perform live in front of 20-30 people. In that sense I don't think there's too much difference between cricket and music, and that's why I'll offer a stern 'work hard!' at the end of one of Finn's tracks, always ensuring to get the words in before the crowd applauds the song.

Finn is my first port of call when my attention turns from the match to the circuit, usually seconds after I exit the field of play. I'll spend 20 minutes in the sheds by myself after an innings, 'reflecting' on how I got out, but in reality, I'm texting Finn regarding our Saturday night circuit.

But Finn doesn't understand why I still play cricket. He hasn't said that directly, but I can tell. He used to at least ask how I went; whether I was a shot at a higher grade, but he's stopped doing that now. Even though I embellished my abilities to him during school — 'Yeah, I basically play state' — I'm a bit more honest with him these days. We lived together for a while, which exposed him to the grim grind of it all. I'd walk in the door on a Saturday evening after yet another dispiriting cricket experience, and there he'd be, on the couch, head down in some rare music publication.

'How'd you go?' he'd ask.

Well, mate. My seven-minute net session on Thursday night facing two slow-medium fifth graders of Indian origin proved the ideal preparation for my 18-ball duck today.

'Yeah, hit 40-odd,' I'd eventually answer, through gritted teeth.

I fell foul of mixing cricket and non-cricket mates once, though. I was in third grade, and we'd just been comfortably beaten by an outfit who'd lipped us heavily over the two-day fixture. We were livid, so we spent the next few hours building consensus that they were, indeed, the biggest fuckwits in the comp. We felt better.

At this point, Bretty suggested we do a Paddingville circuit. 'The birds there are unbelievable!' he reasoned.

There was widespread scepticism, however. Paddingville was not aligned with the prevailing socioeconomic status of our team's rank and file. There were muttered objections, but Bretty held sway, and his promise of 'unbelievable birds' triumphed. Sadly it was only Swampy that couldn't make it; he got red mist again after being given LBW (I immediately said 'that's plumb' from the stands). He steamed off the field of play, smashed a few things in the change room, packed his bag, walked straight to his car and left for home. Under the guise of 'getting drinks ready', a few of us had actually scurried into the sheds to watch the spectacle. He just kept alternating between the words 'Nup' and 'Why?' as he bashed his pad into the wooden bench. By day Swampy is a high-ranking bureaucrat within the Department of Human Services, so I shudder to think of his reaction were he ever made redundant.

A full team circuit is uncommon, so this night came with a sense of occasion. The pub was our marshalling area, and Paddingville our arena. We were like an elite footy team unable to remain still while singing the national anthem, all fidgety energy. Our collective nostrils were flaring. In the words of our 20-year-old private school product, Nathan, it was 'on'. So there we were, 10 of us cabbing it from our middling suburban location into Paddingville. It was rare (in the true sense) for that many of us to be there. Even the private school kids hadn't swanned off to some lavish 21st birthday party in the leafy part of town.

I was in a cab with Bretty, Nuggsy and Bruiser. Bretty sat in the front and dazzled us with an impromptu interview of the cab driver. He covered all the basic territory, from establishing when the driver commenced his shift (3.30pm), to where he's 'actually from' (Australia), whether he liked cricket (he did), and when he finished (2am). Bretty was winking at us all throughout the exchange. I failed to see the humour within any aspect of the conversation, but I giggled along regardless, making sure I at least appeared to know what was going on. The thing is, the content of Bretty's conversations never matter because his shirt always looks so good on him. They're always tight and snug all over, as though he has a custom made body for clothing. His chest looked defined and the correct amount of bicep skin protruded from his invariably short sleeve.

I've got to get big and cut like Bretty, I thought to myself. *Then I would really nail a circuit like this.*

We'd arrived at our bar and slid out of the cab, all adolescent jostling and shoving and hijinks. The excitement had not diminished an iota.

Bruiser picked up the fare, and was startlingly quick to do so. 'I've got it, boys. You can get me a drink,' he warbled in a register one or two rungs below his normal voice.

There was no objection from us. I had ghosted in close to Bruiser as we were initially hailing the cab. He didn't train, hadn't taken a pole in three months, and abhorred playing with the teenagers in the grades below, so he retained his place through gestures like this. We walked into the bar and the team was already there, drinks in hand.

'Any danger of getting here on time?' Deeks growled sarcastically.

Deeks was our captain; he wasn't very funny. He'd been at the club for 14 years, sat on a senior committee of some description, and had won a premiership in second grade six years ago, which he still spoke about. His name had recently been etched on a dilapidated wooden club board in our pavilion for players with over 3000 runs and 100 wickets for the club. There was even a special presentation for the milestone. His face turned a distinct crimson, though, when the MC, our state player, suggested this gave him a career batting average of 14.5. There was uproarious laughter in the venue, some of it quite aggressive. Deeks responded by shouting 'it's 17 actually, check MyCricket!' — a move that failed to stem the torrent of giggles. So it was against this background that Deeks made his remark. As always, we laughed it off. Secretly, everyone was disappointed Bruiser hadn't appeared sooner, because he normally buys the first round of beers and they're usually premium.

The team had arranged tables and seats in the corner of the establishment in almost identical fashion to our formation at the pub earlier. 'Yeah we'll get a good optic from here,' I ventured to the boys, receiving a couple of validating nods in the process.

The two 20-year-olds were nodding with alarming vigour, sharp eyes piercing right through me, which I found disconcerting. Even though I'd made the 'optic' comment, it occurred to me that we were simply mimicking our pub set up, except this time the seats were leather, the tables mahogany and the beers $8.20. Still, optics.

The bar was called Le Bain. It was an intimidating name for our less cosmopolitan teammates, like Nuggsy and Dazza, who saw it as an assault on their very identity.

Nuggsy cornered me at one point, asking with great vulnerability why we had to 'mix with these pretentious posers'. 'Mate, I like a night at Fargo Bar as much as the next bloke, but I'm here being made to drink $20 cocktails, listen to this French shit and deal with birds who take one look at my Jeans West shirt and piss off,' he said. 'What sort of name is "La Bain" anyway?'

A part of me felt like telling him it was actually pronounced 'Le Ban,' but quickly thought better of it. Personally, I was loving the vibe, but nonetheless wary of being too demonstrative about it. Nuggsy's description of the music as 'French shit' couldn't have been more misguided. I welcomed the jazz-infused lounge beats overlayed with classic European singers like Edith Piaf and Nana Mouskouri. As the night went on, those voices provided a welcome soundtrack to a fascinating conversation I had with John, our bookish teammate, who had recently completed his Master of Art Curatorship, and taken up a role with the Australia Council for the Arts. He divulged his plan for developing a new grants model to support artists. I was thoroughly engaged.

Soon, a pivotal moment came when John, upon finishing his white wine, asked what I was drinking. I had to think about this. I snuck a cursory glance towards the group to see whether anyone was looking in my direction. They were all watching Bretty entertain three blondes at the bar, presumably laying hypothetical bets as to which one he'd take home later that night. They couldn't see me over in the dark corner, talking with John about government funding for local thespians, thinking about ordering something other than a schooner of beer.

'I'll have a glass of the white,' I said eventually, in hushed tones.

John stopped, cocked an eyebrow, and stared at me for a few moments before heading to the bar.

As he returned, I felt the need to explain my hesitation. 'You won't believe how often it happens to me mate. The amount of times I ask the barman for a Carlton Draught and some chips, when really I'd much prefer a crisp Pinot Grigio and a cheese platter,' I lamented.

Alan raised his eyebrows, pushed his glasses to the bridge of his nose, and looked me directly in the eye. 'Wasn't it Laertes in Shakespeare's *Hamlet* that said:

This above all: to thine own self be true,
And it must follow, as the night the day,
Thou canst not then be false to any man.
Farewell, my blessing season this in thee!

'Actually, I think it was Polonius!' I laughed.

'Indeed!'

We clinked glasses. This was connection.

I was feeling great after a couple of glasses of Pinot Gris. Suddenly, I felt a vibration in my pocket.

'You about tonight mate? Lounge bar, Paddingville. Mike's doing an acoustic set: Elliot Smith's 'XO' album. The one we listened to last week. Keen?'

Finn's text sent my internal dialogue went into overdrive. I was very keen on his proposal, but I couldn't leave the team. I hadn't hit enough runs during the season to abandon them for a better offer. *Could I possibly convince them to come?* It was an audacious thought, and one that could have huge implications on my social capital at the club. Lounge Bar was around the corner, but may as well have been a world away from Le Bain. Most of the lads were struggling to wrest themselves away from the corner of this bar, but did Lounge Bar hold better prospects? Or were they forever confined to every corner of every establishment, regardless of where they went? No, I'd seen Bretty do some damage away from the corner. But would they have any interest in the music? And what about Finn? He barely has any time for cricket conversation; how would he manage all 10 of us?

I had a nice buzz going by now. I was feeling buoyant, free to be myself. My conversation with John had been illuminating. Maybe I *could* embrace my artistic interests? Maybe I *could* openly prefer aromatic white wine to a carb-y Carlton Draught? Lord knows Finn had been encouraging me to do this for years. Moreover, the boys were struggling here, and much like John had done with me an hour ago, I was about to offer them an option, a lifeline. *Yes, Lounge Bar is a good idea. It's a new path, a new way, and I am going to lead it.*

I'd have to be shrewd to get the boys there, though. I swallowed my doubts and approached the pack, trying my best to embody gruff confidence in my voice. 'Boys. My mate just sent me a pic of his missus. She's unbelievable.'

The woman I was referring to was Finn's long-term girlfriend. She wasn't nude, but it was revealing enough. I knew it was wrong, but the jaw-dropping awe of my teammates was intoxicating.

'Very tidy,' replied Nuggsy, now in a trance, eyes fixated on the screen.

The other boys were similarly engaged, with various primitive sounds and whistles cutting through the classy lounge beats. They were in the palm of my hand.

Is this influence? I wondered. Whatever it was, it felt great. But the next thing I announced was probably even worse than the first.

'Lads, this bird is at Lounge Bar next door.'

'Does she have mates?' Nuggsy asked hopefully.

'Plenty of 'em,' I shot back. I felt like a street rapper delivering the shutdown.

So we went.

'Can't believe there was no bouncer. Great result!' Thommo wailed at me as we bounded into the venue. I didn't know what was worse — his yeasty breath, or the flecks of saliva cannoning into my eye. He was now probably 12 drinks deep, had undone a button on his newly purchased $149 Marcs shirt, and accrued multiple beer stains on his tattered brown leather shoes, bought on sale at YD.

It was a dark bar — full of music posters, dim lights and vinyl music. The carpet smelt of stale beer; Pink Floyd tunes wafted through the band room. This was inner Paddingville, now. Even though we'd only gone around the corner, the demography had changed. I was standing with Nuggsy, explaining why I had no time for Thommo since all he wanted to do was talk cricket, when I spotted Finn on the other side of the room. We caught eyes momentarily — a non-verbal 'hey, man' — but to my relief, he stayed there in the corner, perhaps sensing the situation. Once I'd finished educating Nuggsy about my position on Thommo, I came over. This was Finn, my oldest and dearest friend. He'd been there from the start, and knew me better than anyone. It was good to see him.

'G'day champ,' I said to him, shaking his hand more firmly than normal. 'You remember Nuggsy, don't you?'

'G'day bud,' said Nuggsy, clearly seeking out the social head start. His 6'2" frame seemed to envelop Finn, who took his hand and offered a friendly 'Hi.'

'Where's your missus, mate?' Nuggsy said, a little too eagerly. 'She's unbe*lievable*!'

Nuggsy wouldn't have noticed anything, but the brief glance that Finn shot at me, eyebrows furrowed and eyes ablaze, felt like it lasted a lifetime. He was smart, Finn. In those infinitesimal moments he had made the calculations and realised what had happened.

'You mean Chloe?' he replied. 'Yeah she's here. Have you guys met, or something?'

Finn delivered the enquiry calmly, looking directly at Nuggsy and adopting a look of genuine interest with undertones of suspicion. Finn had no rig, but he wasn't intimidated by grade cricketers in the way I could be. He didn't see Nuggsy as a guy who'd played 42 career first grade games, who'd once lidded the state player in the nets, who you avoided bowling to at training because he had *levers* and could hit a long ball. He hadn't had the opportunity to admire Nuggsy for his rocket arm or occasionally salacious sex tales. To Finn, this was just a bloke with an incongruously tight white V-neck t-shirt, overly firm handshake and limited vocabulary.

Nuggsy laughed. 'Mate I haven't met her, but old mate here showed us a screenshot of that SnapChat pic. Wow!'

Wow, indeed. The blood drained from my face. 'Old mate' meant me. It was an appropriate reference, albeit unintentional. Finn stared at me. He'd sent me that pic a month ago — Chloe had just placed 5th in a beach triathlon, and he'd taken a shot of her, bikini-clad, against the ocean backdrop. Sweat glistened off her tanned, toned body as she stood there, staring directly down the barrel of the camera. *I'm probably going to keep this*, I'd thought at the time. She looked good. But Finn had sent it to me because he was proud, not because she looked good. And now I had re-appropriated his earnest celebration of Chloe into something sexual in order to curry favour amongst my cricket teammates. *Good from me.*

As Finn looked at me, the final moments of that inimitable female solo in Pink Floyd's *Great Gig In The Sky* hovered through the air. I loved that solo.

'Is that right?' Finn asked, his trained voice heavy with sarcasm.

We had been standing in a triangle formation as the exchange took place, with Finn staring at me as he faced Nuggsy. However, he had now fully pirouetted his body to address me, just me. Nuggsy realised something was amiss. He hated confrontations, which made this worse. For someone whose commitment to alphadom was so pronounced, he was now a shrivelled embarrassment of physicality;

all bowed-head, stiff shoulders, darting eyes and overzealous swigs of his bourbon and coke, the loud clinks of his ice only serving to amplify the growing tension.

As this all unfolded, Mike was humbly closing out his cover of *Sweet Adeline*, the first track off Elliott Smith's *XO* album. 'Or any situation where I'm … better off than dead,' he sang, to modest yet respectful applause. Just as Mike was introducing the backstory for the next song, *Tomorrow, Tomorrow*, a sharp, piercing yowl came from the back of the room, causing the band members to look up from the instruments they were tuning.

'Give us *Khe Sanh*, champ! Yiew!'

It was Bretty, boldly calling on Mike to perform a rendition of Cold Chisel's celebrated pub anthem. His ironic song request instantly gave way to three boisterous 'Yiews!' of varying length and intensity from other teammates. The crowd turned around and looked at them, leaning proudly up against the wall, beers in hand, totally oblivious to anything.

Bretty's rude interruption had allowed me time to contemplate my response to Finn. I had done the wrong thing. I knew he'd be livid. Deep down he meant more to me than any of my cricket mates. I really hated upsetting him. But at the same time, I couldn't back down in front of Nuggsy.

'Take it easy, bud,' I blurted out back to him, finally. 'It's a tight rig, nothing more nothing less.'

I couldn't believe that's what I'd said. Finn could have taken exception to any number of words within my belligerent response. He chose the first one.

'*It's* a tight rig?' He looked distressed, but then he calmed. 'Mate, who *are* you?'

It was a good question.

4

LOVE AND ROMANCE

I'd had girlfriends in the past, but none of them 'got' me. They didn't understand my true needs and wants, passions and desires. They didn't know that I need a new stick every year. They couldn't comprehend why on earth I wanted the same body fat percentage as 19-year-old Davo, or that I was passionate about producing the perfect cordial ratio at every drinks interval. And they certainly didn't understand my unshakeable desire to play a slightly higher level of amateur cricket.

No one in the past truly understood these things, but I remained forever hopeful that one day a girl would walk into my life and change me. A lot of blokes seem concerned that their girlfriend is trying to change them into something they're not. I, on the other hand, would have loved a woman to make me their project. I was frightened of turning out like Mick in 10 years' time — an angry divorcee with a terrible drinking problem and abominable skin folds — yet at the same time, worried I'd never get another taste of second grade cricket. It's a cycle that has tormented my lovers (both of them) and myself. As a product of grade cricket, I never really had a good model when it came to maintaining a functional relationship with a woman.

Sure, I'd based my batting technique on stylish icons like Mark Waugh and Dean Jones — and that's taken me this far — but I had never been shown an example of how to love. I remember Dad used to mutter under his breath when giving me throwdowns on Tuesdays after work. He worked himself up into a fury, each throw harder and more aggressive than the last. I could never fully make out what he said, but I did notice he threw a lot more short stuff at me whenever he and Mum were fighting. That's probably why I still hate the short ball.

Anyway, it's usually pretty big news when one of the boys gets a missus. It wasn't like this when I first started playing a decade ago, but now, it's common practice to check out the new girl's profile on Facebook just to see whether there's a rig shot within her first five profile pictures. The best conversations, of course, occur in the stretching circle. Here, any player who claims to have established a successful interaction with a human woman will be accountable to his teammates' questions.

This scenario is where the Chop King absolutely thrives. Firstly, the stretching circle is his domain. He needs 20 ears to listen to his various sexual adventures — in many cases, it's the only reason he's still playing cricket. The stories will almost always involve him drinking for eight hours prior to the moment he actually works up the courage to approach her. When another player mentions that he, too, has recently slept with a woman, the Chop King will immediately feel threatened by his new rival. Suddenly, he's a mere spectator. He'll probably pretend to stretch his hamstrings and yawn nonchalantly in order to effectively feign his disinterest. But since the Chop King is likely the only person to have seen a naked female body in some time, he cannot resist the urge to ask the most obscene questions, despite his fear that the story will overshadow everything he stands for. Sure, we all want to know these details, but he's the only one with the courage, confidence and swagger to ask the big questions. Whether or not these questions are even answered is entirely irrelevant, as he will finish the interview, every time, with: 'Does she have any hot friends?' Here, he is essentially asking: 'does she vaguely know anybody who might let me see them naked?'

Bretty is our designated Chop King, but despite his numerous sexual encounters, I can't really tell if he's happy or not. On the surface, he seems happy. But I like to think of him like an onion: he has many layers, and he's usually making a woman cry for some reason. Bretty's a great guy to go out with because he'll talk to anyone, but he's pretty loose. I once saw him drink seven tequila shots through his eyeballs before snorting six lines of salt. He's probably been the closest thing to a role model that I've ever had.

The story of the Chop King bares mild similarity to the titular character in Shakespeare's *King Lear*. Here, the elderly monarch is preparing to handover his power and wealth to his three daughters, with the one who loves him the most set to inherit the majority slice. When the Chop King 'retires' — and by that, I mean he gets married, or is struck down by the HIV virus (whichever comes first) — he must find a successor. There will be no shortage of suitable candidates, but the one who has publicly shown that he is capable of taking up the mantle — verified 'chops' are key here — will be handed the throne. It's more than likely that this fellow has served a lengthy apprenticeship as the Chop King's wingman, perhaps having even participated in some form of group sex together. While others may dispute the Chop King's decision, unlike *King Lear*, the team will abide by the leader's call. There can only ever be one true Chop King at a time.

Chop Kings never hold the throne for more than three years. That's not an official thing; it just seems to be the way it is. Kind of like how the NRL competition is cyclical. Anyway, the first Chop King I met was this bloke called 'Chappers'. I never actually knew his real name — even though he played in a higher grade than me — because everyone always just used to call him Chappers. Even the police called him that. I was just 17, with only a few games of fifth grade under my belt, when Chappers took me under his wing. I don't know what he saw in me, but he said I had 'potential'. I was confused because he had been calling me Tim for about a season and a half. After a string of low scores, Chappers eventually ended up in my team one week. It was then that someone finally told him my name wasn't actually Tim. Chappers looked me dead in the eye. *'Yeah, I know.'*

Anyway, Chappers was a real pants man. Doctors would later go on to describe it as a 'serious and debilitating addiction to sex and pornography', but gee it was great fun when he'd tell us about the women he'd 'had'. In hindsight, he did have some very unusual, anti-social habits. He went through a rather obnoxious phase where he'd urinate on the bar whenever we were at a nightclub. He didn't even really seem to have a reason for it. From about 2003–2005, I never saw him use a toilet. He would just unzip his pants and start pissing. What's even stranger is that I never saw him get in trouble for it. Often, he'd manage to get a round of free drinks after explaining his honest mistake. As I was only 17 at the time, it was very confusing to see a 29-year-old man not only committing to this obscure practice, but genuinely revelling in it.

Another trick he had was to time how long he could chat to random women before they'd realise his penis was hanging out of his fly. It usually took about three minutes, but I reckon 15 percent of the time it actually led to a chop — and only twice were the police involved. Those are fucking good odds if you ask me. All of these things aside, Chappers had a lethal cut shot and was a good first slipper, so we brushed these incidents off as 'classic Chappers', rather than treating them as the serious psychological issues that they were.

Bretty used to have a pretty serious girlfriend until he decided to have a season overseas. All the boys encouraged him to break up with her because doing long distance when you're an overseas pro is a bit like wearing a helmet when you're getting throwdowns: completely unnecessary and will only get in the way. Besides, it was off-brand for the club's most celebrated *chopsman* to be in a serious committed relationship. So he decided to break up with Mel and took off for a frivolous summer in the north of England.

As it turned out, he shouldn't have listened to us idiots. Mel was a beautiful girl, a real stunner, and smart, too. I think her family was from money; they always used to look after Bretty really well. But by the time he'd come back from the UK, having, in his words, 'smashed half of England', Mel had met a really nice man from the accounting firm she worked at. She was engaged six short months later and, before long, they'd started a family. In the years that passed, Bretty was chopping birds left, right and centre. He always claimed he was fine, but after 13 beers he'd start talking your ear off about Mel. I certainly couldn't offer him any advice or perspective, but I did like it when he talked to me because there was always the off chance he'd introduce me to someone.

As any Chop King will tell you, it's rarely about 'quality'. In fact, Bretty always said: 'It's a numbers game.' Of course, he was referring to women, not his batting average. After about 30 beers one Friday night, Bretty once slurred in my ear: 'I'd rather have sex with ten "3s" than three "10s". To me, he's got that entirely the wrong way around, but it fits his personal maxim of just trying to sleep with as many women as he could. He followed that bit of insight up with this grotesque statement: 'The ugly ones always do way more stuff.' He vomited five minutes later on the dance floor and scored the worst 7 off 42 I've ever seen in my life the next day.

Another thing Bretty always spoke about was group sex. Specifically, his desire for 'roasting'. Roasting, essentially, is a consensual act where two men sandwich a willing woman between each other during a threesome. Other lurid names for this despicable act include 'spit-roasting', 'Eiffel-towering', 'gangbanging' and, among cricketing circles, '*bowling in partnerships: pressure from both ends.*' It was the zenith of sexual activities and Bretty dearly wanted it — more so, I think, than he wanted to move out of his parents' basement.

Frustratingly, I could never verify any of Bretty's stories since the woman in question was never seen again. Also, he didn't even own a phone, so it's not like he was getting their numbers and following up for a date that Friday night. In fact, I don't think I ever heard him refer to a woman by her first name. I wanted to believe these stories were true, though, so they were.

To be fair, all the boys lied about their sex lives. Even I did. One's social stocks can rise dramatically on the back of a good sex story. Every dressing room that I've ever been in relies on someone getting pissed the night before and bringing back something to the herd as an offering. It's classic hunter-gatherer mentality. You can't have 11 blokes in your team who spent the night watching online porn in between stints on the PlayStation, even though that's how I spend 90 percent of my weeknights. And that's why lying is a critical part of any dressing room. To the expectant crowd, there's no difference between fantasy and reality — only perception. On Saturday morning, no one cares if you stayed at home the night before, read Tolstoy's *War and Peace* and went to bed at 9pm. If you tell them you had sex outside a kebab shop at 4am that morning, then that's exactly what you did. When it comes to stories, it's all about how it does at the box office.

I didn't lose my virginity until I was 22. God, it feels so good to get that off my chest. I've been carrying that secret around for a very long time. Of course, no one at the cricket club knows this. As far as they know, I was chopping birds before I even hit puberty. But for the first few years of my grade cricket career, I listened intently as my teammates recounted thousands upon thousands of impossibly positive sexual experiences. And yes, I'm ashamed to say that I even told a few of my own, riffing on bits that I'd heard in the stretching circle over the years, changing a few key details to make the story my own. I was the Edouard Manet of the grade cricket sphere: borrowing ideas from my artistic forebears in a bid to gain acceptance in the Parisian art scene.

But deep down, I was scared of the opposite sex. Being among these hyper-masculine cricketers had distorted my ideal of the perfect female partner. If the stories told in the stretching circle were anything to go by, it seemed like everyone was having sex with porn stars. Meanwhile, I was still furiously masturbating to hard copy Penthouse magazines from the 1970s, which I'd stolen from my Dad's secret stash. I guess there is something delightfully innocent about that. I'd been out on every circuit, but was yet to perform a publicly celebrated chop of my own. I was beginning to think that something was 'wrong' with me. I wondered for a fleeting moment whether I might even be a homosexual, but despite the constant exposure to naked men, I felt nothing. Sure, I was deeply envious of blokes with good rigs and quality 'lids', but I wasn't attracted to them. I just wished I had their work ethic and genetics.

To be honest, I can't think of a single openly gay bloke I've played with or against over the many years I've been involved with grade cricket. It's possible they do exist at some of the more progressive clubs, but as with most professional sporting environments, I suspect many blokes are forced to mask their true selves in order to fit into the feudal system. It really does beggar belief that there isn't one single gay man in the competition. There was one bloke who opened the bowling for us for a season, who always used to criticise Bretty and others for objectifying women in the stretching circle. For a while we thought he might have been gay, but turned out he was just really passionate about gender equality.

Nuggsy once told me a story about a couple of ex-players who he'd suspected were secretly having a 'thing'. Guiseppe Cataldo was a stocky right-hander; Richard Moreland a tall, stylish left-hander who still holds the club record for the highest individual fourth grade innings. They opened the batting together in second grade for several seasons, having struck up a great left/right combination at the top of the order. Following a devastating semi-final loss at home, the team decided to drown their sorrows in the dressing room for a few hours, as is the grade cricket custom. At one point, Nuggsy and Damo went to relieve themselves outside, when they spotted Guiseppe and Richard having an intensely private conversation over in the shadowy corner of the car park. All of a sudden, they leaned in for a passionate kiss, which lasted some three to four seconds. Nuggsy and Damo looked at each other, momentarily stunned. *Did that just happen?* They'd had about 13 beers between them, and light was fading fast, but they were nonetheless convinced of what they'd seen. They never mentioned it publicly, though, so the incident was eventually forgotten. Anyway, Guiseppe took an interstate job that off-season and was never seen again. Rick's married with three young children and occasionally fills in for fifth grade when they're short of players. I just hope they're both happy.

Then one night, it finally happened. I was out on the circuit with the lads after a dispiriting innings loss to our cross-town rival. One of the positives of losing by an innings is that you usually get to start drinking in the early afternoon. So by 6pm, I'd had about 13 beers and was up for anything. She was at least 15 years older, with a gruff, throaty voice that spoke of a life-long cigarette habit and a slight (but manageable) alcohol problem. Her skirt was short — dangerously so — and she had a thick mane of red hair reminiscent of Nicole Kidman's 'do in *BMX Bandits*. She looked good from 15 paces — and importantly, she had received the tick of approval from my teammates.

'Red heads go off in the sack,' Nuggsy whispered in my ear, as we ogled her from the bar.

To be fair, Nuggsy said the same thing about women of all hair colours, ages and races. Brunettes, blondes, dark hair, red hair; white, Asian, Indian — to Nuggsy, they were all 'gagging for it'. I briefly wondered whether Nuggsy's attitude towards women had been shaped by the fact his mother had abandoned the family when he was just eight years old. Whether this was the reason he was seemingly on a quest to have sex with every living, breathing female, as part of some misguided Oedipal revenge. However, this was not the time to be contemplating Freudian psychosexual theory. This was the time to lose my virginity.

Soon enough, we locked eyes over Bruce Springsteen's *Dancing in the Dark*, which Nuggsy had selected as his third song on the jukebox. I danced across to her, vibing the eighties classic, arms flailing, collar popped, sleeves rolled up in homage to The Boss. Feeling confident, I mimed the lyrics ironically — *'can't start a fire without a spark!'* — and she laughed. I liked that she laughed.

A few hours later, we arrived back to her house, drunk and disorderly. She directed me to the bedroom and ducked into the bathroom to 'freshen up', giving me a chance to gather my thoughts. *Shit, what am I doing here?* I scanned the room. I gathered that this was once a marital bed, a room of happy memories. Framed pictures of young children adorned the bedside table; the sheets were silk satin, soft to the touch, presumably expensive. This felt incredibly adult; naturally, I felt out of my depth. I hoped that she was divorced, or at least separated.

'The condoms are in the second shelf,' a voice yelled, coarsely, from the bathroom.

I took a deep breath and lunged my arm inside, grabbing a fistful of the things. I looked at them in my hand. I was not sure what to do with them, but I understood they were necessary and a pre-requisite for this specific act. Of course, when re-telling this experience to my teammates at training the following week, I would neglect to mention that I used protection. I'm yet to hear a sex story that involves the use of condoms. Wearing a 'lid' is seen as a sign of weakness and such conservatism will surely dilute the tale itself.

She appeared from behind the door, naked, determined. It became apparent that this was her show and I was merely a giddy participant.

With Germanic-like authority, she ordered me to undress. I did, awkwardly. A few minutes of bumbling foreplay ensued. This was no different to the way I usually start all my innings: scratchy at the start, and never really 'in'. The whole time, I was thinking about how I would describe this encounter to my teammates at Tuesday's training.

And quickly, it was over, soon as it had begun. I had lost my virginity; shaken the bastard off. An incredible sense of relief swept over me as I hauled myself off this poor woman. I slept soundly, dreaming of how I would describe this encounter to my teammates at Tuesday's training session. As I walked out the door the next morning — taking care to avoid her six-year-old son, silently eating cereal in front of *Saturday Disney* — I felt a new man. I was now — if only for a fleeting moment — the Chop King. I'd had sex with a woman. It was the most adult thing you could do, have sex with a woman — and I had done it.

I was finally one of the boys.

5

AN ENGLISH SUMMER

I didn't know what I wanted. Part of me thought that I could still make it, but another part of me saw what Finn and others were achieving outside of this self-imposed prison. It made me wonder whether there was indeed more to life than just cricket. For the first time, I was no longer sure that mere runs and wickets held the key to happiness.

Over the many years spent traveling to distant cricket fields, along the same interconnected motorways, underneath that same southern sun, I'd lost what 'making it' even meant. When I was a kid, I was the best backyard cricketer of all my mates, which led me to think an eventual test call-up was a mere formality. The kids in the street were simply no match for me, as I pummelled their limp-wristed bowling to all parts of the cul-de-sac. This dead-eyed determination and dominance is probably why they only let me play that one time, and generally rebuffed all my subsequent advances for friendship, but fuck I was good that day. At that point in my life though, 'making it' meant playing under lights in front of 90,000 people at the MCG. Young kids chanting my name, wearing my One Day International shirt. I wasn't interested in women, fast cars, or being on the cover of magazines (unless we're talking about *Inside Edge* — the greatest cricket magazine ever produced). I just wanted the youth of a nation to love me. That's all.

But after a few years of adult cricket, I realised that it would take a lot of hard work to play professionally. It was *hard*. It seemed that everyone else was *good*. I was all of a sudden a tiny, insignificant fish in a giant pond full of alpha male humans. And so over time, 'making it' gradually went from playing in the Boxing Day test, to earning a state contract, to getting a game in first grade. Now, all I wanted was a middle order spot in second grade and a serviceable batting average of around 20.7. And to go one day at training without being 'champed'.

Growing up, the only time I heard about 'grade cricket' was on the odd occasion an international player made a return to the game through this avenue. In most cases, the player in question was gingerly returning from a lengthy spell on the sidelines through injury. The media always described this 'park cricket' as a bit of slap and giggle — just a few blokes rocking up and giving it a go. While not an altogether inaccurate observation, I was shocked to find that the grade cricket system boasted blokes who could bowl in excess of 140km/h and smack it 150 metres. That there were some exceptionally talented cricketers out there, lighting up suburban cricket ovals despite still stinking of last night's rum. For a while, I'd hang around the first grade fixtures on Sundays, praying for someone to do a hammy so I could fill in as a substitute fielder for 11 overs, but the call never came. My dreams and subsequent direction in life were thrown into absolute disarray.

Obviously, I had to get better in order to 'make it'. I couldn't just spend my six months off in the winter playing amateur football and eating sausage rolls for breakfast. I needed to spend those months working on my front-foot press, honing my rig, working on my base tan. Perhaps a season in England was the answer? There, I'd gain the edge required to move up the grades. At the very least, it would allow me to postpone adulthood for a bit longer. I was afraid of the prospect of full-time work, plus the girl I was seeing at the time wanted me to take our relationship a bit more seriously. I needed to get away from these adult realities and focus on my cricket. Yes, England *was* the answer.

I'd heard that most English clubs generally contract one 'overseas' player each season, in the misguided hope their foreign talent would boost the club's chances of promotion up the leagues. I've never really understood why random strangers pump money into amateur cricket clubs. There's literally no return on investment, ever. But for me, a successful season in England would serve as a badge of honour; one I could wear proudly upon my return to Australian grade cricket. I'd put it on my cricket CV and thrust it in front of the selectors ahead of round one. Perhaps I'd put it on my actual CV as well, just to fill in the glaring gaps.

Damo and Robbo had about 20 seasons in the UK between them. Robbo had done his 13 seasons back-to-back — 26 summers in a row — but had never returned to the same club, which spoke volumes about him as a bloke. Damo, for his part, had spread his seven or eight seasons over a few different stints. Immigration pulled him up on the last trip back, with a four-hour interrogation revealing he'd never held the correct visa. He was sternly instructed to never return.

I bailed Damo up after training one day, hoping he'd have some ideas on how to get a gig overseas. 'You've spent a lot of time playing in the UK, Damo. Got any advice for a young buck looking to spread his wings and improve his cricket?'

Damo put a fatherly arm around my shoulder. 'Well, mate. For starters, you want to get your flights and accommodation paid for. The pound is a lot higher than the Aussie dollar, so make sure they look after you financially,' he advised.

Damo, an expert at shifty trades and negotiating himself in and out of situations, was a real schemer. At the time, he was ripping off the local grocery store by about $200 a fortnight by 'phantom scanning' certain items at the self check-outs. I wouldn't trust Damo with a lot of things — talking to my girlfriend, holding my phone, driving me home after a couple of post-training beers — but he was a great bloke to have in your corner for these sorts of situations. He also had some amazing pipes on him, which I casually squeezed every time we got in a huddle after someone had taken a wicket.

According to Damo, clubs in the northern parts of England would be able to offer higher match payments than those in the south, but this was offset by the fact pitches were 'increasingly shit the further north you go.'

'London's got a great circuit, plus the birds there are way better. Definitely get yourself down to Brighton, that's on the south coast, you'll bloody love it down there. Up north, it's all about how young you can have a kid and get those government benefits. Sure, do some trips up to Newcastle and Liverpool for a good night's circuit, but personally, I'd be looking to base myself in London.'

Damo seemed torn. He wanted to tell me to do one thing, but then remembered how wonderfully appealing the exact opposite thing was, and recommended that I should do that too. It made me wonder how on earth he'd forged a career as a risk management consultant.

'The Australian accent will go a lot further up north, though,' he continued. 'You'll clean up on the circuit there. In London, every other prick is Australian, so you won't be able to work that angle as much.'

I wasn't really sure if he was offering advice anymore or just reminiscing wistfully on the days when UK immigration would let him into the country. I was also somewhat aghast at the idea that any woman could find Damo's voice attractive. But if Damo's rough, nasal accent was deemed exotic, then perhaps my slightly more cosmopolitan — yet undeniably Australian — accent could also work a charm with the ladies?

'Actually, you should get in touch with Bridgey, I'm pretty sure he was captain of his club down in Surrey. I'll give you his email address,' Damo concluded.

Nicolas Bainbridge was a lovely English bloke who'd been at our club a few seasons before. He joined us after finishing his teaching degree back home, in the hope of doing a bit of travelling before commencing full-time work at some pretentious all-boys school around London. One of those ones where the kids wear waistcoats and straw hats, carry British nobility titles like Earl, Viscount and Baron, and all look vaguely inbred. 'Bridgey' played most of the season, but was shafted just before the finals for 'Brownie', a talented yet erratic youngster who left the club soon after to pursue a career as a DJ. I heard Brownie's now doing the early morning shift in some grim underground nightclub and being paid in ecstasy. Good work if you can get it, I suppose.

A few days later, having sent a generic email to around 200 UK clubs with little to no response, I decided to send Bridgey an email. He made a few calls around and within three weeks, I had signed a deal for the English summer. With the contract now confirmed, I revelled in telling my mates the story of how a stack of UK clubs had chased me for my signature. It was a high-stakes bidding war, and after allowing several shortlisted clubs to court me, I'd finally settled on the club that 'seemed the best fit'.

Yes, England would give me the chance to make up for years of mediocrity. On foreign soil, safely distanced from the insidious grade cricket ecosystem, I'd have the freedom to reinvent myself. I couldn't wait to get over there.

After a long, tortuous flight, made easier by the unfettered access to free alcohol, I stumbled into the arrivals lounge at Heathrow, much like how Nuggsy often used to wobble into the dressing rooms after a big night on the cans. There, I saw a tall, dark haired man holding a cardboard sign with my name on it. I strode toward him and offered a casual 'G'day'. He, in turn, extended a long, muscular arm towards me, presenting an intimidatingly firm handshake with strong eye contact. I instantly assessed his body fat percentage to be less than 12 percent.

'Hello. I'm Robert Hargreaves. An absolute pleasure to meet you!'

This bloke was the *poshest* bloke I'd ever met. He stood there smiling, resplendent in red chinos, a blue and white striped business shirt and expensive looking loafers. His hair was neatly swept to the side; his dimpled cheeks, the cleanest of clean-shaven. Part of me fell in love with him a bit, to be honest, but I knew I needed to assert myself.

'Cheers, champion. Let's hit the road, shall we?' I bellowed confidently, looking over his shoulder.

Here was this nice man who'd volunteered to put me up in his house for six months, rent-free, having taken the day off work to collect me from the airport, and I had instantly 'negged' him to let him know that *I* was the fucking alpha dog in this relationship. I felt a slight tinge of regret as I picked up my luggage and followed him to the car.

Robert's house was about an hour south of Heathrow airport, allowing us a bit of time to get to know each other. I instantly liked this charming, erudite Englishman. He had a delightful little stammer, which gave him the air of a Hugh Grant character. I gauged him to be in his mid-20s; his blemish-free skin and excellent diction gave the impression he was from good aristocratic stock, probably an *Old Harrovian,* or some shit. He was a skilled and interesting conversationalist, but when he started banging on about 'Thatcherism', I felt a bit out of my depth. As always, when threatened intellectually, I reverted the chat back to cricket.

'So, where's our home ground, mate?' I asked.

'Not far, actually. We can head there now and grab a pint, if you like? I think some of the other chaps might be knocking around.'

'No dramas, superstar.'

I was absolutely exhausted from the 24 hours of international travel. I wanted nothing more than to walk into Robert's spare room and crash into the heavenly manchester on the lavish king-size bed that I imagined would be waiting for me, but in fear of being labelled soft, I assessed that I might have to drink alcohol in order to impress everyone.

We wound our way through the quaint town before ascending a steep hill and turning right into our home ground. It was an absolute picture. The outfield was plush; a healthy, verdant hue. I thought about the outfields back home in Australia, all barren, desecrated from drought, littered with miscellaneous objects — condoms, chip packets, you name it. One time, I dived to save a boundary, only to realise I'd fallen on a used syringe. It was a nervous three-month wait for the blood test results. But here, I might even be compelled to dive to save a single. A quintessentially English pavilion sat at one end of the ground; an even square timber construct, with a steeply slanting roof covered in thick green moss. An analogue scoreboard sat squarely and succinctly above the pavilion doors. The next thing I noticed was the size of the boundaries. They were 45 metres at best. I figured that here, my weak forearms could easily muster a few *maximums*.

Robert and I walked into the pavilion, where James, Matt, Patty and Robbie were already waiting for us. I was surprised that they introduced themselves using their actual birth names. Back home, the new English recruit would be introduced to 'Choppy', 'Starkers', 'Fingers' and 'Bumper'. I was also thrown by how similar they all looked. All were clean-shaven, with glorious hair parted neatly to the side; each decked out in a neatly pressed, slim-fit dress shirt, comfortably untucked, exuding a casual elegance. Here, there were no topknots, no shaved sides, no ridiculous Mohawks. No Tarocash shirts or extra-small V-neck t-shirts. Just crisply ironed shirts and smooth, well hydrated faces.

Fuck. These blokes must all have jobs.

I wasn't wrong. These guys were starkly different to my teammates back home — not just in appearance, but in what they did for a living. Matt was a 30-year-old surgeon, while Patty was a brilliant young lawyer. James was a history teacher at a posh English school. Robbie was doing a PhD in biochemistry, having received a substantial government grant to aid his studies. It was a far cry from the retail workers and online gamblers I was used to playing with back in Australia.

I had braced myself for a hostile reception as the overseas import, but these lads were just so friendly and hospitable. I remembered back to the last time we had an English bloke playing at our club — Neil something-or-other, a really friendly guy who just wanted to see a new part of the world and play a bit of cricket. That year, Australia won the Ashes 5-0 in a blowout series. A bunch of my teammates thought it would be funny to spray paint Neil's car with the series score-line on the driver's side door. The car wasn't even his and it cost him about $1200 to fix it. Nobody chipped in to help him out. We all referred to him as 'Five Neil' for the remainder of the summer, too. The ringleader, Dazza, said it 'served him right for being shit.' Neil averaged over 60 that season and didn't drop a single catch. I'm pretty sure he gave up cricket when he got home to the UK, settling into a stable, well-paid job at HSBC.

I was relieved to find that, in contrast to Neil's experience, I would be welcomed with open arms at my new club.

Our opening fixture landed on the first Saturday of May, and it was fucking cold. Everyone else seemed to be revelling in this 'unseasonably warm' weather, though. Incredibly, our opening bowler was wearing a short-sleeved shirt. Judging by his pasty pigment, this bloke desperately needed the vitamin D. I wanted to give him the nickname 'Casper' or 'Whitey', but decided I should exercise some sensitivity on my first day. If he ever visits Australia, he'll have six nicknames before he gets off the tarmac.

Earlier that day, we'd been rolled for 210. I was bowled by a length delivery that I should have come forward to — a ball that would have come through at chest height back home. Up until about round four, we were basically playing cricket on rolled moss. Even so, my stylish 31 earned me several pats on the back in the dressing room. I had announced myself in the world of English cricket.

The opposition required 40 from the last nine overs, with just three wickets in hand. It was tight. It was tense. I didn't actually see any of it, though, because I was on the mid-wicket boundary squinting at moving silhouettes 55 metres in front of me. It was genuinely pitch-black by the time the game came to a close — a real shock for me coming straight out of the Australian summer, where it's 25 degrees and blue skies at 6pm. I'd love to give you the ball-by-ball, the blow-by-blow, but I've got literally no idea what happened. I didn't even move in between overs. It was only 5pm, but it might as well have been midnight.

At one point I heard the crack of ball on willow — that unmistakable sound of summer — followed by a prolonged cry of 'CCAAAAATTTTCHHHH!!' It was a sequence that I recognised immediately; a pivotal moment that could dictate a season, a summer, only I had no idea who was bowling, whether it was a left- or right-handed batsman on strike, where I was fielding — let alone where the fuck the ball was. I instinctively cradled my head and got in the foetal position, hoping that by making myself as small as possible, I wouldn't be struck by the ball. After a few seconds, lying on the ground, a merciful shriek rang out.

'YEEESSSSSSSSSSS!!!!'

I hauled myself up off the cold turf and sprinted blindly towards the sounds of back slaps and banter. Unfortunately, the team's huddle had just about dissipated by the time I reached the pitch. Now, I faced a fresh dilemma. *Where was I fielding? How do I get back there?* I scrambled over to the other side of the field, frantically trying to get into position before the next ball was bowled, only to tumble into a patch of stinging nettles. At this point, having observed the patch earlier that morning, I realised I'd been standing 15 metres on the wrong side of the boundary. It was my first encounter with these green, leafy bastards, and my hands stung for the next 10 minutes or so. But the pain vanished when Patty cleaned up their number 11 to secure our five-run victory. It was a cracking finish, by all reports.

I wasn't sure if anybody had seen me. The other 10 blokes seemed to have cat-like night vision, but nobody questioned why I'd been fielding at deep gully for 45 minutes, let alone why I'd positioned myself off the actual field of play for half an over. It was 5.30pm when we shook hands with the opposition. By then, the temperature had dropped to around four degrees, and I was looking forward to sitting in the shower with nine jumpers on.

As we walked off the field, Robert bellowed over to me, 'You ready for some lagers, old boy?'

'Mate, I've been frothing for a circuit ever since I got here.'

Robert looked at me as if I'd just spoken to him in a different language. I guess that in many ways, I had.

'Don't tell me we're not hitting the circuit?' I thundered.

'Well that depends, old boy. What is a *circuit*?'

I put my arm around his giant frame and pulled him in close. 'Just you wait. We're going large tonight, champion!'

After a couple of obligatory beers with the opposition, we hopped back to our home ground to commence the team circuit. I jumped in the backseat of George's three-door Polo, squirming to get comfortable alongside three boisterous teammates and four large cricket kits, as we chugged lagers and sung along to Radio 1. George was about 6'6" and 145 kilograms, which made his tiny, European car all the more incongruous. Despite his hulking physique, George was a sweet, gentle man. What's more, he had a car and always offered to give you a lift, so he was usually the first name on the team sheet for an away game.

I'd dusted off about five pints by the time we stepped out of George's Polo. This tactic was two-fold. First of all, I needed to get a good buzz going in order to artificially raise my confidence levels, much like a first grader does after smoking some lower-grade rubbish in the 'shit net'. Secondly, the beers were way cheaper at the clubhouse than anywhere else in town. As such, I graciously grabbed the first round — *'it's on me, lads'* — a move designed to show that I wasn't afraid to dip into my wallet for the boys. In reality, I'd left my wallet in George's car and didn't get it back for three weeks. Still, I got the first beers in — putting it on my bar tab — earning myself a strong degree of social capital.

I'd longed to sample the sights and sounds of an English circuit. But with it being so cold here, I suspected there wouldn't be much skin on show. Oh, how wrong I was. Not long after we arrived at the chosen venue, I spied a reasonably attractive blonde sitting at the bar with a friend. In order to get things happening, I tried an old trick I'd learned from Bretty — the 'accidental' bump. Bretty once told me that 90 percent of his chops had come about through the accidental bump, so I was keen to try it out for myself. Having duly grabbed her attention after a crude hip-and-shoulder, I offered a light-hearted faux-apology.

'Sorry, love!'

'That's quite alright, darling. Where are you from? Are you *Australian?*' she asked.

'God, not another fucking Australian,' the other bird grumbled.

'Sure am, darling. Did you know that we ride Kangaroos to work in Australia?' I tried, immediately regretting the lame choice of words.

'Come on, mate. *I'm* from Australia too! I moved here about six years ago, actually,' the blonde replied, now thoroughly engaged.

Suddenly, I had found myself in conversation with *two* ladies. This never happened back home! Throughout the exchange, I remained acutely aware that the lads were watching me from the other side of the bar, egging me on in their distinctively British way. Every now and then I'd shoot them a knowing glance — *'it's on here, lads'* — before turning my eyes back to the girls, feigning interest in whatever it was they were talking about. Was I *this guy*? I always wanted to be this guy.

Katherine was a short, blonde woman of an indeterminate age. Her skin had an even, natural tan — a refreshing change from the orange palms and splotchy legs that seemed strangely ubiquitous in England. Her friend, meanwhile, seemed largely disinterested in the conversation. She kept butting in with the phrase, 'so ... anyway', which seemed like her way of telling me to fuck off.

Not a chance, love. Do you have any idea of how much social capital I'm gaining by talking to you two?

I tactfully exited the conversation after 10 minutes to re-join the lads. Before long, 'last drinks' were called, and it was time to head back to George's flat to check out the day's scores online. As the summer rolled on, this would become a regular event: we'd get hammered on lager and cider, order three large 'Meatlovers' pizzas, six garlic breads, and scroll through the results until the early hours. I didn't really like Meatlovers pizza; I was just happy to be around teammates who weren't trying to alpha me at every opportunity.

But just as I made my way towards the exit to embark on this ritual, I spied Katherine there, sitting alone.

'Where's old mate?' I slurred.

'Who? Oh, Sarah? She left about an hour ago,' she said with a tinge of sadness.

This was a crucial moment in my season. The tension was palpable. Here I was, on a proverbial 99 not out, and I'd been given a half-volley on my pads. All I had to do was keep calm and do the right thing.

Play straight here, mate. No need to be a hero. Just knock it into the on side for a single and raise your bat to the applause in the morning.

I'd been standing there in front of her, not saying anything for about 30 seconds; just playing the situation out in my head, before she finally broke the silence. 'Are you taking me home then?'

'Absolutely, love!'

As we passionately made out in the back seat of a traditional black London cab, my mind went into overdrive. Specifically, whether my 31 runs would be good enough to get me in the local newspaper tomorrow morning.

'Talk to me!' Katherine breathed in my ear, jolting me back into reality. This was a difficult act to carry out — her tongue had already commenced its adventure down my mouth. I couldn't figure out if I was turned on or scared of this woman.

'Talk to me!' she pleaded, once more. 'Your accent is so sexy. Talk to me!'

Her pleas were quickly becoming commands.

'What do you want me to say?' I was overwhelmed, but desperately trying to play it cool, like a number four batsman in early at 2-5 on a green deck.

'Just say anything. Tell me what you bought at *Sainsbury's* the last time you went?'

I was so confused. She was Australian. I was Australian. *Why does she want me to read out my fucking shopping list?*

'Umm, shit, let me think. Bread, butter, marmite. Marmite's not nearly as good as Vegemite, but it does the job I reckon. Fuck, we need some milk too, now that I think about it ...'

At this point, I was completely distracted from our amorous embrace, and genuinely thinking about the contents of my fridge.

'Mmmm ... that's so hot. I need you right now,' she practically moaned.

I didn't know what the fuck was happening. This was the most blatant case of homesickness I had ever seen. This poor girl needed a flight home as much as she needed company for the night. A few minutes later, the cab pulled over to the side of the road. The driver looked in his rear view mirror like a voyeur peering through a hedge. I snuck a sly look at the cab fare and felt vaguely sick.

'Sorry love, but do you reckon you can pay for the cab? I just realised I left my black AMEX behind the bar and I don't have any coin on me ...'

I woke the next morning hung over and disorientated, the result of drinking pint glasses for the first time in my life. *Where am I? This*

isn't Robert's sumptuous linen! As I rolled over to my side, I saw a mound of sheets moving up and down next to me, a muffled snore emanating from under the covers. The floor itself was a sea of clothes; a lace bra hung knowingly from a chair, the spilt contents of a handbag resting underneath.

Ah, that's right. Circuit. Chop. Result.

I scampered out of bed, careful not to wake my conquest, and made my way over to my phone. It was only 6.43am, but I needed to make an escape. My shame showed no bounds. I had to get out of there before any awkward conversations could take place. I thought back to a recent conversation I'd had with Damo. For some reason, his 'thing' at the time was to take something from a girl's apartment after a one-night stand; a souvenir to brandish in the stretching circle. This seemed like the ideal opportunity to impress Damo, who, I must remind you, had played first grade. His validation was worth seeking. I scanned the room for something small I could take and show the boys. Toothbrush? A pillow? Suddenly, *bingo!* I spotted the television remote control and slipped it into my pocket. I tiptoed over to the front door to make my inglorious departure. Before stepping out, I took one final look back at Katherine, still sound asleep. Should I wake her up with a goodbye kiss and organise a catch up? No, that would be wrong. Instead, I bowed my head, pushed her television remote control a little deeper into my pocket, and turned the door handle.

As I sat there on the train, staring into the middle distance, I felt increasingly remorseful. I berated myself for running out on Katherine without at least asking for her number. Why had I allowed myself to be influenced by Bretty's dubious rules for handling women? She seemed so lovely and down to earth. *We could have Skyped her family together.* I allowed myself a deep sigh and closed my heavy eyes.

I'm still going to tell the lads about this.

My first and only Sunday match was a memorable experience. I had been asked to fill in at late notice, having been sold by the promise of 'time in the middle' and 'easy runs'. Despite my acute hangover, I jumped at the chance to play on yet another quaint English cricket ground. But things were a bit different in the Sunday league, I soon discovered. Upon arrival, the first thing I noticed was the outfield. I wasn't entirely sure how we were expected to play cricket on a ground that sloped like the Swiss Alps. Secondly, there was a *tree* on the field, just 10 metres from the pitch. What would happen if the ball hit the tree? Was this commonplace in England, to have trees on the field? I could obviously never tell anyone back home that I'd been playing on a ground with a tree on it.

Back home, warm ups are bloody intense, covering all the major disciplines. Throwdowns, slips practice, T-drills, you name it — all done with aggression, at 100 percent pace. Here, an old bloke was casually hitting soft catches to the rest of the team standing in a semi-circle formation, hands in pockets, chatting amicably amongst themselves. As we went through this lacklustre fielding drill, I looked over to see the two captains sharing a laugh at the coin toss, practically holding each other arm-in-arm like old college buddies. A few minutes later, our captain returned to us, miming the one-handed 'front foot defence' gesture to indicate we were batting first. An ironic cheer burst out and we all shuffled back to the pavilion to 'prepare' for the match.

Chris and Aidan opened the batting for us. Chris, a retired barrister, wore buckle-up pads, while Aidan used a bat with no branding on it that'd been crafted two decades before I was even born. I was told that they were both 'former county players', but I had my doubts. Neither looked like he was sponsored. Their opening bowler was wearing a white button-up business shirt and tennis shoes; he trotted in from about eight paces and gingerly rolled his arm over for the first ball of the match. The ball slipped out and landed three metres off the cut surface. The wicketkeeper, an enormous man wearing batting pads and gardener's gloves, missed the ball on the sixth bounce and the opening pair scampered through for a bye.

'Great start, lads!' I shouted, eyes darting around for a response.

The comment was met with utter silence, a reaction that confounded me. If this happened back home there would have been nine Facebook status updates about it. Meanwhile, the other opening bowler - a man who looked well into his 60s — was sporting a brown belt to keep his trousers up. I couldn't believe what was happening.

This was fucking *village*.

I came in at number four with the score perilously positioned at 2-15. Without too much hassle, I helped myself to a run-a-ball 30, my sizzling strokeplay dazzling the eight or nine spectators in attendance. I was batting with Ciaran, a 50-something entrepreneur. He was more than happy to just give me the strike so he could continue his lively conversation with the umpire; an arrangement that I was more than comfortable with. The 11-year-old bowler wasn't causing me too much concern.

Soon, a new bowler came into the attack. His name was Douglas

Chesterton, a WWII veteran, well known to all throughout the competition. According to legend, Douglas had gone to fight the Germans at the tender age of 13. But at 86, he was the frailest second-change bowler I'd ever seen in my life.

Here's my chance. This bloke is fucking ancient!

He walked in from about three paces, giving the impression it genuinely pained him to roll his arm over. Amazingly, the ball had no revolutions on it. Literally, the ball did not revolve once. It was captivating in its serene stillness, floating through the air like a plastic bag in the wind. It was a good thing he was bowling downhill, or it might not have made the full 22 yards. I respectfully patted the ball back down the wicket, prompting a rapturous response from the stands.

'Well bowled, Douglas!'

'Cracking stuff, old sport!'

'Really good start, Grandad!' the 11-year-old shouted from his position at fine-leg.

My watchful forward defence wasn't out of respect for Douglas' decorated war career; a man who'd lived a rich, full life fighting for King and country. I merely defended his first delivery to get a handle on him. *To get his measure.*

The next ball mirrored the first, but this time I skipped down the wicket and launched it back over Douglas' head for arguably one of the biggest sixes of my life.

Don't bowl there, Dougie!

I'd expected the shot to draw roars of approval from my teammates. Instead, it was met with ear-splitting silence. Douglas' two overs cost him 58 — ironically, the same number of soldiers he was credited with saving during a historic two-day battle with the Nazis.

Soon enough, I tickled one around the corned to bring up my first UK hundred. I took my cap off and ran towards the pavilion, arms aloft, breathing in the applause. This was my moment. My chanceless century was met with sporadic half-hearted applause from the three spectators present, but I didn't care. I'd posted a massive score for these blokes to defend. This was guaranteed to get me a round or two in the bar after the match, surely?

My dismissal in the following over is still something that frustrates me to this day. I pressed forward to a full-length delivery, the ball brushing my pad on its way to first slip. The umpire stood there for a long time, almost waiting for me to walk, before giving me out. I was livid. Fucking livid. I did my best to hide it, though — only throwing my bat once as I walked off the field. I'd been robbed of the chance to notch up a double ton.

Our bowling innings was a complete mismatch. I'd snagged myself a position in the cordon, ready to sledge these pricks, feeling invincible. Still riding the high from my batting performance, I laid into their opening batsmen with unbridled delight.

'Come on, champ. Get on with it!'

'You know it's a one-dayer, don't you?'

'This bloke's weak as fuck outside off!'

'Don't be scared to go upstairs here, David!'

The worst sledging I copped all season came from a 'northern' opening bowler, who'd beaten me all ends up on four consecutive deliveries. On the fifth, I nicked it between slip and gully for four. As I braced myself for a vicious verbal tirade, I was surprised to see him smile, shake his head slowly, and mutter, 'You jammy bastard!'

In Australia, sledges would be far more aggressive in nature; toe-curling insults delivered dead-eyed and deadpan without a trace of humour. Once, one bloke genuinely claimed to have consummated his relationship with my mother — even providing specifics on the location and date of the tryst — but I didn't recognise him, and Mum always invites any new friends to dinner.

We ended up winning the game by about 230 runs or so. Both teams sauntered off the field, arm-in-arm, off to the bar for a tipple or two. I thought it was strange that no one bought me a drink — or even asked me to play again — but I had certainly made an impact as the ruthless overseas player.

Over the next few months, it rained constantly. During the delays, my teammates used this time to engage in intelligent conversation about topical issues. Back home, rain delays were spent playing silly games in the dressing rooms, just another chance to assert oneself as the alpha dog. I took these contests very seriously — often more seriously than the actual game itself. I averaged 11.4 in my last season, but I did score a double ton in a game of dressing-room French cricket during a two-hour rain delay. Upon reflection, that was certainly my highlight of the summer. I also noticed a difference in the way my new teammates acted during the post-match showers. Back home, Nuggsy used to play a game where he'd see how long he could urinate on a teammate before they realised. He'd drop the soap in front of a new kid, uttering some kind of slimy jailhouse phrase to our collective laughter. But here, showers were far less intimidating.

After one particularly miserable draw, the old umpire walked into the communal showers, revealing one of the smallest penises I've ever seen. 'Here he is. Here's the big man!' I announced to the shower block, with relish.

To my surprise, no one blinked an eye. I didn't get it — this would have got a great laugh from all the lads back home. Frankly, I was perplexed as to why we were even showering with the umpires. This bloke didn't give an LBW all game and now we're supposed to be mates? Why did he even need a shower after officiating a 45-over game in 10-degree weather?

While there were several key differences between the two cricketing cultures, some things remained constant. Young men worried about how they looked. It was a more obvious thing in Australia, and maybe the better weather meant that you had your rig on display more often, but British men still spent hours gazing into the mirror, dreaming of bigger pipes, broader shoulders and decent abs. No one gave a fuck about legs, though. That view was global. I also saw a lot of questionable tans that season — not just on the circuit, but also amongst my own teammates. I suppose it's a reflection of western culture and the desire to met societal expectations, but everyone here wanted to be brown. One teammate secretly divulged to me that he'd been taking 'tan tablets' — over-the-counter medication scientifically formulated to turn your skin a darker shade. I didn't even know this was a thing, but I guess we don't have to worry about tan tablets back in Australia because our summer lasts for longer than 14 days. Back home, there was always one bloke in the team who smelled suspiciously like coconut, having surreptitiously applied *Reef Oil* instead of actual sunscreen to get that golden glow for the Saturday night circuit. But tan tablets? That'll fucking do me.

Anyway, with just one match to go in the season, I had given us a fantastic shot at promotion into Division 1. We just needed a win against the second placed team, who we'd heard were without half their regular players that week — one bloke had accidentally planned his stag weekend in Ibiza a week early. We just needed to turn up and take the chocolates.

I'd recently reconnected with Nuggsy over various social media platforms. He seemed in a dark place; his texting had become more and more rampant as the days wore on. These were all desperate showings from a bloke struggling with his own identity. During cricket season, Nuggsy was the heart of the cricket club. But in the off-season, he was just another unemployed battler with an unfortunate gambling problem.

One morning, I got a text from Nuggsy at 2am.

'I'm coming over there, bud. Just booked my tickets. Let's do a European circuit!'

I don't think Nuggsy realised how big Europe was. You couldn't just do one big Euro circuit without some serious savings in the bank. Back then the Australian Dollar was still quite low; the resources boom yet to make a significant impact on the exchange rate. Unless he'd won big on the pokies, there was no way he could afford this trip.

'These idiots at the bank have just given me a credit card! It's got 10 large on it!'

I humoured him — *'Looking forward to tearing up Europe with you, Nuggler!'* — despite having zero confidence he could follow through with any of these plans. Nuggsy was terrible at organising himself. There's no way he had gone into a bank, successfully applied for a credit card, visited a travel agent and booked a return ticket to England. But two weeks later, Nuggsy rocked up at Robert's doorstep at around 1am on a Tuesday. To this day, I have absolutely no idea how he got his address — he certainly never asked me for it.

Robert opened the door, bleary-eyed, only to see a 6'2" Australian grinning back at him, wearing thongs, board shorts and a blue wife-beater singlet. 'Nice place ya got here, champ! Look after these bags for me thanks, legend!'

Nuggsy was like an excitable puppy, bounding his way back into my life again.

The final Saturday of the season beckoned. Emails had flown around during the week on how this would be 'the defining match in the club's history'. But by this point, Nuggsy had already convinced me to go on holiday with him, and I was on the Greek island of Magaluf, reading these emails on a sun chair. I later heard the boys were unable to find a replacement for me in the final match. They were forced to declare their innings closed after the ninth wicket fell, just five runs short of victory. I felt bad at the time, but Nuggsy kept me distracted for long enough to forget all about it.

Unfortunately, the Nuggler was struck down by a particularly nasty bout of gonorrhea after partying a little too hard with the locals, and the promise of a 'European circuit' ended up being a guided tour of the continent's worst hospitals and sexual health clinics.

Still, my tan was amazing for round one back home.

6

THE CAPTAINCY

I was first handed the captaincy at the age of 12, selected (unanimously) to helm our local representative team. Of course, back then there was absolutely no strategy involved. I was the best player in the team and therefore the captaincy was automatically mine. It was probably the last time that a meritocracy system actually worked in my favour. Our U12 coach, Charlie Chandrasekhar, used to give me signals from the boundary. Whenever he felt a fielding or bowling change had to be made, he'd make the appropriate gesture. Once, an umpire banned him from the match for 'coaching' after he was spotted signalling to me that I had three fielders behind square. We had to give his son, Sunil, a lift home that day. I'm pretty sure that every team had a Charlie Chandrasekhar pulling the strings on the sidelines. No 12-year-old kid knew how to set a field.

But as an adult, it's a far different prospect maintaining control over 10 fully grown men, who vary wildly in terms of their ages and personality disorders. I still remember the first time I captained a grade cricket team. Deeks was out for six weeks with a 'hamstring injury' (to those in the know, he was secretly serving home detention for benefit fraud) and I was given the task of steering our team to the finals. Suddenly, I was exposed to a whole new world of admin that I didn't know existed. Turned out that captaining a grade cricket team required a lot of effort. I had to organise the covers on Thursday and Friday night. I was tasked with writing the match report and logging all the weekend's scores into MyCricket. I had to deal with pushy parents who thought their son wasn't getting a fair go. I was required to take part in 'selection meetings', and endure an endless stream of phone calls from the chairman of selectors and other faceless, peripheral committee members, all keen to vehemently discuss possible team line-ups during business hours on a Monday.

And that's only the off-field stuff.

My first coin toss as a grade cricket captain was possibly the most embarrassing moment of my life. Collar up and chest out, I strode coolly to greet the opposition skipper at the pitch, presenting my hand for the customary introduction while maintaining strict eye contact, all in adherence to expected gender norms. However, to my own peril, I completely misjudged the trajectory of my hand. I was late and shallow on impact and, as a result, his massive mitt clamped around my four fingers, crushing them together like a vice. I resisted the urge to squeal in agony. It wasn't a good start.

The trick to a good handshake is to get as *deep* into the other person's hand as possible. The perfect masculine handshake will involve both parties establishing good depth and a firm grip on each other's hand. You should aim to make strong, aggressive contact with the sinewy webbing between thumb and forefinger — the impact should feel bouncy — and complete your grip with fingers clasped confidently around the outside of the other's hand. A certain rising action is recommended (*i.e* start low and swing upwards and 'into' the hand). Again, eye contact is essential. I cannot stress this enough. You should be able to do this in your sleep. A good shake will set the tone for your entire relationship with that person, so you best get it right.

As we made terrible small talk — *'how are you lads going this season?'* — I shot a quick glance at the opposition warming up. Fuck they looked switched on. Bats and gloves had been lined up neatly against the fence. The top-order batsmen were doing throwdowns, middling everything. The fast bowlers had measured out their run ups and were running through their paces on the side pitch. Just as I turned, a single stump was sent cartwheeling, much to the delight of the vocally supportive wicketkeeper. The mood looked positive, buoyant. I then looked over to see what our blokes were doing. They were nowhere to be seen. On cue, I heard an eruption of guffaws and hollers from the dressing room, the echoes carrying all the way to the pitch. They were still in the sheds listening to Bretty's enthralling chop story from last night's circuit. I caught the start of the tale before heading out for the toss, but honestly, it's too crude to repeat. Let's just say Bretty had 'made' a woman 'do' something last night that she certainly wouldn't be telling her friends about.

As home skipper, it was my honour to flip the coin. I had chosen a shiny 50-cent piece to mark the occasion. It was the first time I'd tossed a coin in three years, when Nuggsy and I had flipped whether to do a cab run or not, so I was excited. But just as I went to launch the coin into the air, it slipped from my grasp — a consequence of the greasy 7-11 sausage roll I had eaten just moments before in a failed bid to stave off my hangover — and fell on to the ground. A false start.

'Sorry mate, should I flip again?'

'I'd say so, champ,' my adversary blithely responded. Upon the word *champ*, he made a loud, perfunctory pop of his Extra chewing gum, which served as a telling exclamation mark.

Shaken, I focused hard on my second take, flinging the coin high up into the air, comically so.

'Tails,' the skipper called.

After what seemed like an age, the coin finally came down to earth — only to inexplicably wedge itself in the pitch.

'You're fucking kidding. Any danger of actually flipping the coin properly? Fuck me,' he said, with startling venom.

Embarrassed at the loss of face, I bent down to pick the coin off the ground. But to my horror, it had buried itself deep inside the turf. *Shit, how is that even possible?* With all my effort, I tried to pry it out. I was on all fours, grunting as I desperately sought to extract the coin, but to no avail.

'Mate, it's jammed in there,' I explained, looking up at the skipper apologetically.

'Oh my fucking god,' he bellowed. 'Come on, out of the way, give me a go.'

He crouched down to evaluate the situation, like a father inspecting a flat tyre for his mechanically illiterate son. I hoped that he would struggle to get the coin out of the turf too, but alas, not so — he dextrously plucked the coin free of its mire using just his thumb and forefinger. I was mortified at the sheer ease at which he had performed this seemingly impossible task.

'Seriously, champ, you've got weaker wrists than my missus,' he smirked. 'Now how about *I* toss and *you* call, how does that sound?'

I nodded silently. The humiliation was complete. I couldn't even perform a simple coin toss. It was a new low.

Up it went.

'Heads,' I called.

Naturally, it was tails.

'We'll have a bat, thanks *championship*,' he blurted, with obvious relish.

He had just alpha-dogged the shit out of me at each and every turn. The word *championship* — an absurd faux-extension of the word 'champ' — only added salt to my gaping mortal wounds. In retrospect, I should have just packed my kit and headed home there and then. Really, I should have just *retired* there and then.

'Would have bowled anyway,' I muttered under my breath out of sheer habit.

'What was that?' he fired back, in a frightening register, like an Irish backpacker outside *Scruffy Murphys*, 12 beers deep and stinging for a confrontation.

'Nothing, mate. Good luck for the game.'

'Yeah, whatever.'

And with that, I put the 50-cent piece in my pocket and walked back to the pavilion. In the distance, I noticed my teammates straining to see whether I had won or lost the toss, eagerly waiting on my requisite signal. I remembered all the times that my captain had walked back after the toss. We would always wait anxiously to receive confirmation as to whether we were batting or bowling. I suddenly understood why captains enjoy milking every second of time as players desperately await the outcome of the toss. The power is immense. Of course, when indicating the outcome of the toss, there are two dominant options: understated mimicry of a forward defensive stroke, or nonchalant seam-up wrist flick. I'd seen some other variations before — a tap on the knee or an uncouth 'wanking' gesture to indicate that we're 'batting' — but these were far less common. On the more obscure end of the spectrum, I once saw an opposition captain run full-steam from the pitch towards his teammates and launch into a whole-hearted mock delivery, as if he were Dennis Lillee — follow through and everything — before casually telling his opening batsmen to 'chuck the pads on, lads'. I went with the traditional, nonchalant seam-up gesture, having kept my teammates in suspense for at least 60 seconds. A collective groan ensued — we'd be lucky to keep this side under 450 on this deck.

We finished our warm up and went into the sheds, with just five minutes left before the start of play. I knew that I was obliged to say a few words to the team, but what would they be? I was not a natural orator. I lacked the physical presence and polish of a Barack Obama. Was there any point, though? Looking around, I saw a bunch of disorganised adults frantically trying to get their shit together in time for the session. 'Got any sunscreen, Damo?' 'Can you spot me some zinc, Trav?' 'Has anybody got a hat?' I could have recited Lincoln's Gettysburg address in full — *'four score and seven years ago ...'* — and these blokes wouldn't have batted an eyelid. As such, I fell back on the versatile, tried and true maxim that all grade captains are well familiar with.

'Let's just fucking work hard and get these cunts out!' I screamed at the top of my voice, just as the old umpire poked his head into the room.

My outburst startled him, but he managed to compose himself

well enough to mutter the patented phrase he was being paid $60, every Saturday, to say: 'We're on our way, lads.'

My imploration to 'work hard' was largely met with a murmur of agreement. 'Boys!' someone added, meaninglessly. 'Big session here, lads!' said another. Job done. So out we went.

Most captains stand at mid-off in order to support the bowler, for reasons I have never understood. If you get to choose where you field, why not pick the best spot on the park? Why go vanilla when you can have Neapolitan? As such, I parked myself in the cordon — at second slip, no less — and delegated this supporting role to Nuggsy. Nuggsy was a former grade captain and a bit older, too, so he had a bit of experience. But mainly, I liked the idea of having a right-hand man, or *consigliere*. In the *Godfather* series, Tom Hagen plays the role of *consigliere* to Don Corleone. Nuggsy bares some similarities to this fictional character in that he, too, is the son of an abusive alcoholic. However, that's pretty much where it ends. Nuggsy is not mild-mannered and rational, nor has he ever been described as a 'voice of reason'. However, Nuggsy — like Tom Hagen — was viciously loyal. I wanted Nuggsy as part of my leadership group.

Nuggsy was in charge of 'chat'. I knew that I lacked both the wit and the energy to continually roll out tired, meaningless platitudes over the course of the day. Prior to the captaincy, my on-field chat was mostly akin to a U-shaped parabola: initially positive, then awfully negative ($y = -4$) before an upbeat surge immediately prior to drinks. To me, fielding is pretty much a civic duty; you spend six hours, on your day off, vocally supporting teammates for whom you harbour a deep-seated hatred. I found it hard to get excited about. But urging teammates to 'talk' (read: create white noise) and 'keep energy levels up' was Nuggsy's forte. He was also the best shiner of a cricket ball that I'd ever seen, even if he did have a worrying tendency to rub the ball directly against his genitals.

In addition to these attributes, Nuggsy was extremely skilled at buttering up the umpires — and seemed to know all of them on a first-name basis. In fact, it was Nuggsy who first told me that while on-field chat with umpires is forced and self-serving, it is nonetheless essential. As such, he advised me to apply elements of seduction theory in order to win them over. Having not read *The Game* — Neil Strauss' best-selling 'bible' on how to pick up women — I was initially unfamiliar with the concept of 'negging'. For those who haven't read the book — and I strongly urge that you do if you really want to understand women — negging is where you give underhanded compliments to women in order to get them to eventually sleep with you. By insulting their hair, choice of dress or friends, it forces the woman to 'prove' herself to you, or so the theory goes. It has a particularly great effect on women who suffer from low self-esteem. Umpires suffer from a tremendously low level of self-esteem, too, by virtue of the fact that they are umpires. As such, you should look to engage in light-hearted horseplay with them at all times. Negging him about the amount of sunscreen he's wearing — which is always inversely proportional to his decision-making ability — is a good place to start. Like all of us, all they really want is to be loved. So your missus still doesn't understand why you spend your whole weekend playing cricket? Imagine how an umpire's girlfriend must feel. Seriously, imagine being an umpire's girlfriend. He'd rather officiate a shit game of cricket than spend a gorgeous Saturday afternoon with you.

Of course, if you go to the effort of buttering up the umpire only to cop a shit LBW moments later, you should definitely spend the next six hours subverting his authority.

But back to the game. We bowled some loose stuff early, allowing their opening batsmen to get off to a strong start. I wanted to take our 34-year-old opening bowler off after his second over, but each time I said 'I'll give you one more over', he'd shoot me a vicious glare, as if to say, 'Take me off and I'll fucking kill you.' Sure enough, he tore his hammy halfway through his fifth over. He would later blame me for his premature retirement. To be honest, I think I did him a massive favour. Last I heard, he'd given up the drink and tied the knot with his high-school sweetheart, who he'd emailed one weekend after realising he literally had nothing to do in his spare time.

We went to the drinks break in a bit of trouble at 1-90, one bowler down. I desperately wanted to deploy the 'let's just fucking work hard and get these cunts out' phrase, but I felt I should keep that in reserve lest I dilute its effect by wearing it out too early. Instead, we just stood around drinking cordial and nodding at each other. Fuck it was a good ratio though. That team always did good ratios.

After the break, I decided to bring a leg-spinner on. It was a risk — this bloke hadn't bowled consecutive dot balls since 2005 — but one that I felt we needed to take. I decided to park myself at short-cover to look strategic. In reality, I just wanted to get in the batsman's eye-line on the off chance I might put him off. I don't have a good cricket brain — never have — but from that day on, I always set a short straight mid-on or mid-off to make it look like I did. Of course, our leggie got absolutely pumped and I was forced to take him off. At 1-140 after 30 overs, we were in a fair bit of trouble. They say that a team should look to double their score at the 30 over mark, when playing a one-dayer. I don't think I've ever been part of a team that has chased 280. Even in a two-day fixture.

We managed to snare a couple of key wickets over the next 15 overs, which helped drag the run-rate down considerably. Unfortunately, I had miscounted the number of overs left, which meant our best bowler had finished his 10 over spell with five overs still to go. I told the lads that I'd made the mistake because I was used to playing 45-over cricket in England (a complete lie, but it reminded everyone that I had done a season overseas, so it was a good shout). Anyway, it meant that we needed to fill five overs somehow. I decided that, as captain, I'd step up and bowl three of the remaining five overs. I hadn't bowled in years, but why not? I was captain — and I could literally do whatever I wanted. I could have stripped naked and bowled left-arm Chinaman from around the wicket if I wanted to. Incidentally, that did happen once in an intra-club social game after a few beers. I took 1-21 off two overs that day.

The opposing captain had arrived at the crease. He was tall, broad shouldered, with a rig seemingly carved out of stone by Michelangelo himself. Regardless, he was batting and I was bowling, so I had the chance to enact some revenge following the embarrassing coin toss incident earlier that morning.

'Lot of pressure on this bloke now,' I shouted from my bowling mark.

'Not really, it's 3-235 with five overs remaining,' he called back. I noticed both umpires giggling over the witty riposte. Fuckwits.

God, he's right. There is absolutely no pressure on this bloke at all.

In I steamed. There was only one thought on my mind. *I have to bounce this bloke.* It was my solution to everything. If I could bounce my boss, I would. I dug the ball in as short as I could, grunting as I exploded through the popping crease. I looked up quickly only to see that my opponent was in a perfect position to execute a hook shot.

The ball sat up — courtesy of my lack of pace — to fall into what is commonly known as 'the zone'. I'm not going to lie. The sound of his bat on ball was almost orgasmic. If there's ever been a better shot in the history of cricket, I am yet to see it. The ball sailed off his bat and fell handsomely onto the tennis court adjacent the ground, some 120 metres away. It bounced into the net during a seniors' mixed doubles match, disrupting the point. They looked around in utter disbelief, shocked that a human could hit the ball that far. Meryl, one of the old ladies playing tennis that day, took seven attempts to underarm the ball back over the fence. With each failed attempt, the opposition team roared their approval. 'Yiew.' 'Yiew.' 'YIEW!!' Fuck, it was humiliating. *Why did Meryl have such a shit arm? Couldn't she just open the gate for Nathan to come in and get it?* I really wanted that ball back.

As we waited on Meryl, the captain walked down the pitch to stand next to me, admiring the chaos his glorious shot had prompted.

'More of that, please,' he whispered in my ear.

And with that, he performed a stylish pirouette and returned to his crease, denying me the chance for a witty comeback. Not that I had one to give. I never had one to give.

I managed to complete my over without conceding any more boundaries, but the damage was done. I threw the ball to young Nathan, instructing him to keep things tight. He did. In the end, they scored 3-254 off 50 overs. It was going to be a tough chase, but do-able.

As all batsmen know, four — or 'second drop' — is the most premium position in the batting order. Firstly, your openers and first drop protect you from the new ball. You are the queen in chess —

versatile, elegant, and generally afforded a great deal of respect by the opposition. Experienced chess players know that the queen becomes more of an asset late in the game, once the pawns, rooks and bishops have done all the hard work. Secondly, by the time you come to the crease, the first change bowlers are usually on, the ball's a bit older, and runs are generally easier to come by. And thirdly, and perhaps most importantly, it's just good to say, 'I bat four.' Some of my greatest cricketing heroes were those who batted four. Therefore, I would bat four.

But in keeping in with the general tone of the day, we started terribly. Bretty went out in the first over and all of a sudden we were 1-0. I was in next, and scared. As the valuable queen, I was not yet ready to venture out onto the board; I craved protection, security. But who would protect me? I asked one of the new blokes, Trav, if he felt like going in at four. He could be my sacrificial lamb. My pawn.

'It's a really good opportunity for you to show the selectors what you can do up the order,' I lied.

Trav, in his first year of grade cricket, was young and naïve, so naturally he leapt at the opportunity. A few overs later he was in after our other opener's off-stump went cartwheeling. Trav was out first ball, LBW without playing a shot. Three weeks later he would quit cricket and take up golf full-time. With Trav gone, we were three for not many after just eight overs. The game was basically lost at that stage; the opposition's chat at an all-time high. I needed to find someone else to protect me for a bit longer. But whom could I turn to?

'Nuggsy, can you go out and *do a job* for us, mate?' I implored.

There was nothing more Nuggsy loved than being asked to 'do a job' (except when it was in reference to actual employment, which he detested).

'Sure thing, skip,' he replied.

Nuggsy ran to the dressing room, strapped on his pads in world-record time, and was quickly out to the crease. I breathed a little easier.

At the completion of the over, the 76-year-old umpire turned to the pavilion and yelled, with a trembling voice, 'tea in two overs!' This, of course, was our cue to prepare the afternoon tea spread. I ambled in to the kitchen to see what the lads had brought with them today. It was an underwhelming effort to say the least. The nutritional balance was way off. Seven of our 11 blokes — myself included — had chosen to purchase pizza-flavoured Shapes from the 7-11 on the way to the ground. This wasn't a deliberate ploy, either. Just a grim coincidence. There's nothing worse than seven packets of Shapes on a hot summer's day.

I decided that from now on, I'd use whatever influence I had as captain to ensure the team was selected based on its ability to provide a diverse spread. I calculated that we would need two or three youngsters, who lived with their parents, to bring a diverse mix of healthy, nutritious treats — watermelon, pineapple, frozen oranges — along with thoughtful home-baked goods. Jam scones, ANZAC biscuits, that kind of thing. A little bit of effort went a long way. I still remember the delightful *croque monsieur* with béchamel sauce that Dazza's wife made us back in 2001 before the divorce. In the 67 games we'd played since their bitter separation, Dazza had brought plain-flavoured Doritos every single time. It was like he'd lost the will to live. Now, whenever I see a bloke bringing plain Doritos to a match, I wonder whether I should just ask him, 'Are you OK, mate?'

A couple of cashed up professionals like Bruiser would be handy, too; these blokes could be relied on to splurge on Tim Tams, Michel's Patisserie cheesecakes and other store-bought luxury items. Of course, we'd also need one anally retentive bloke who would prepare small, perfectly cut sandwiches (preferably in small triangles). I'd have to bring John back up from fifth grade for that. The rest of us useless bastards could provide various thoughtless snacks like Shapes and plain-flavoured Doritos. Maybe even some Nacho Cheese Doritos if we were feeling particularly creative.

Anyway, we made it to tea without losing another wicket. The players filed off the field and straight into the tea room, like soldiers reporting to the mess hall. I dearly hoped that our meagre spread would pass muster with the opposition. But immediately, my worst fears were realised.

'Shit spread!' the alpha captain announced to all within earshot.

It was a bleak but accurate assessment — and indicative of our club in general. Only the successful clubs went to the trouble of providing nourishing tea spreads. At these clubs, friends, wives and girlfriends were welcome at games; a friendly spirit was cultivated both on and off the field. We weren't one of these teams. We had finished last in the Spirit of Cricket awards ever since the initiative was introduced.

All of a sudden, I heard Nuggsy's guttural voice pop out of nowhere. It was a command rather than a request, directed firmly at the opposition captain.

'Take your spikes off in the clubhouse, *champ*,' he boomed.

Firstly, this room was not a 'clubhouse'. It was simply a random room that happened to sit awkwardly between the home and opposition change-rooms. There were a few plastic tables and chairs scattered arbitrarily. A single bar fridge sat against the wall, leaking from the base, small tributaries snaking their way across the concrete floor. If anything, it perhaps resembled a really shitty kitchen. But a *clubhouse*, it was not. To me, the very term 'clubhouse' implies splendid mahogany furniture, carpeted floors and private functions, an element of prestige and exclusivity. I'm pretty sure I saw Deeks spit on the ground in the 'clubhouse' earlier that day, so it wasn't the most salubrious of venues.

We all waited for the captain's reaction. Would a physical confrontation ensue? Would someone have to step in and separate these two brutes?

To my surprise, he responded with an apology. 'Sorry, bud. Lads, spikes off in the clubhouse,' he instructed his teammates, slowly.

I don't know what shocked me more — the fact that the captain had apologised to Nuggsy for his *faux pas,* or that he'd called him 'bud'. I wondered what his response would have been if I had been the one to call him out. I dreaded the thought. I guess Nuggsy had been around the traps for a while. He always knew a few blokes from every team we played, regardless of which grade he was in that weekend. As such, he did seem to garner a fair bit of respect, all things told.

'Mate, how come he called you "bud" and me "champ?"' I asked Nuggsy, earnestly.

'Bud, he doesn't respect you. That's why you've got to hit runs today, to show him that you're the big dog!'

Nuggsy's pep talk strengthened my resolve, yet again. *Fuck it,* I thought. *I'm going to hit some runs today.*

Nuggsy and Walshy had been in for a while. We were about 3-120 after 30 overs and needed a bit over six runs an over to get there, but I was confident. Walshy had been batting really well. Now into his 40s, this club legend and former first grader was now indisputably in his twilight years. But fuck, his technique was good. In fact, every single thing about Walshy screamed 'I have played first grade cricket for several seasons.' His creams looked great on his slightly stocky figure, fitting snugly in all the right places. His facial hair — a dark, bushy yet un-ironic moustache — was enviably masculine. The way he stood there, one leg nonchalantly crossed over the other, helmet under his arm, casually chatting to the umpire, was just *so fucking cricket*. Some people just looked like cricketers, and Walshy was one of those blokes. I wasn't one of those blokes.

Even though I'd played with Walshy for a couple of seasons now, we were still yet to bat together in a game. I'd always wondered what it would be like to chat with him between overs. I often dreamed that Walshy and I would bat together in a run chase one day. He'd give me advice on what the bowlers were doing and how to best exploit their weakness; I'd tell him to 'work hard'. He'd tell me, 'You're doing well, son. Keep it up. I'm proud of you.' One day I brought this up with my psychologist, who then spent the next 60 minutes asking me about my relationship with my father.

Nuggsy soon holed out in the deep. I sucked in a deep breath, popped my helmet on and walked through the squeaky gate on to the field. As I came past Nuggsy, I offered him the mandatory 'well batted, mate' — even though he had thrown his wicket away at a crucial stage with one of the ugliest shots I've ever seen in my life — and made my way to the crease. I looked up to see whether Walshy would be meeting me halfway to provide some intelligence on what the bowler was doing, as was the lower grade custom. Alas, he was in his crease, chatting to the umpire, looking *so fucking cricket*.

'Two legs, thanks Simon,' I called to the umpire. I didn't know what 'two legs' meant (still don't), but I always took guard there anyway because it gave the impression I'd spent a season in the UK.

'Yes, that's two legs. And it's Gavin, actually,' the umpire shot back.

Shit, not a great start getting the umpire's name wrong.

The first ball, a gentle in-swinger, drifted on to my legs. I managed to get a bit of an inside edge on it, enough to see it trickle down to fine leg for a single. I was away. One run off one ball. 100 percent strike rate. Fucking brilliant.

At the end of the over, I walked down the pitch to meet Walshy for a chat. Walshy had over 20 years of grade cricket experience and I was looking forward to mining all of it during our time out in the centre together.

'Hi, Walshy. What does this bloke do?' I enquired, referring to the bowler I was about to face.

More than likely he was just your average 115km/h seam bowler with little-to-no movement in the air or off the deck, but it was mandatory for me to at least ask. I sat back, eagerly awaiting Walshy's in-depth, articulate analysis of the bowler, pitch, and match situation.

'Just keep going, champ. Work hard,' was Walshy's succinct reply. He sniffed loudly, turned around, patted the wicket a couple of times, and returned to his crease.

I shouldn't have been surprised by Walshy's unwillingness to engage in conversation. The only topic I'd ever heard him confidently hold court on for more than a minute was sports betting. He was a few years older than the rest of us and, as such, there was a bit of a generation gap. While the young kids would be on their smartphones, trawling through the latest 'hook up' app for a cheeky match or two, Walshy would be rifling through the TAB section of the paper, checking the race guide. He'd often have his earphones in while waiting to bat, listening to the Group One racing at Moonee Valley on his Walkman. He was old school. But Walshy could bat. His technique was excellent. He had scored over 10,000 runs for the club — mostly in first and second grade back in the 1990s. He didn't need to share this experience with me. He was in the business of scoring runs and wasn't here to make friends. In contrast, I wanted to make friends *and* score runs. Both were proving elusive.

We batted together for about 10 overs in complete silence. After a few overs, I realised it was futile to even engage in eye contact with Walshy — let alone an active dialogue — so we entered an unspoken mutual agreement to concentrate on our own games. In between overs, we'd just walk down the wicket and stand next to each other, looking in opposite directions, saying nothing. After the initial shock, I actually enjoyed the gruff, emotionless masculinity of it all. Eventually, Walshy got a good one and nicked off for a well made 60-odd. With 10 overs to go, we were 5-190 — needing about a run-a-ball to win. I was 18 not out and, all of a sudden, could sense a rare double: red ink *and* a win.

My new batting partner was Timbo, our wicketkeeper. He breezed out to the centre, his long, ridiculous hair flailing in the breeze under his floppy-brimmed Greg Chappell hat. These locks, so long, dark and straight, gave him the appearance of a Native American warrior. A Native American warrior, albeit one with a shit rig, who was wearing baker's whites and a Greg Chappell cricket hat.

'OK, Timbo. I'll take most of the strike since I've got my eye in. No stupid runs,' I said sternly.

Timbo shot me a quizzical look. I wondered whether he had even computed the brief. Earlier that day, I'd noted his incorrect use of the word 'pacific' (mistaking it for the word 'specific'), which had earned a stern rebuke from Bruiser ('Pacific's an ocean, champ'). I'd heard from some of his contemporaries that he'd repeated eighth grade three times. It's fair to say he wasn't the sharpest tool in the shed. It's even fairer to say that he was absolutely fucking stupid.

'Yeah, all good mate. Work hard,' he responded in a high-pitched 21-year-old voice, after what felt like an eternity.

As Timbo and I parted ways, I saw the opposition captain — my nemesis — approach the umpire. He took his cap off, revealing an enviably bouffant head of hair, and handed it to the umpire.

'Here you go, Gavin,' he said cheerfully.

Fuck, look at the close relationship he has with the umpire!

I returned to my crease, ready to stare down my opposite number. This was my chance to perform a truly celebrated captain's knock. As he steamed in, the words *'captain's knock, captain's knock, captain's knock'* ran through my head on a bizarre loop. I guess there are worse things to have in your head while batting. I had the Spice Girls' number one hit, *Wannabe*, in my head for an entire season as a 12-year-old.

The first ball was a bouncer that angled into me. Keeping my eye on the ball the whole way, I arched my back like a limbo expert and ducked under it with consummate ease.

'Plenty more of that to come,' the captain sneered at me.

Despite the voice in my head screaming at me to retaliate with equal arrogance, I held my fire. It was the most restraint I'd ever exercised in my entire life. He looked at me, willing me to bite back. At least 10 seconds passed before he finally, shrugged and turned around.

'Tough guy,' he remarked loudly, to sporadic laughter.

There is nothing more annoying than a player who doesn't

respond to sledging. Normally, I'd take the bait big time, but on this occasion — and especially given my humiliation at the coin toss — I thought it wise to avoid a verbal stoush. I thought back to how I'd told Nuggsy to 'do a job'. Now, it was my turn to perform a task for the good of the team.

In he came for the second ball. Again, a bouncer. Again, I ducked under it with minimal effort. In fact, the ball was so far over my head this time that the umpire called a wide.

'You're fucking *kidding* me!' the bowler shrieked.

'No I'm not, Steven. And that's two for the over, by the way,' the umpire fired back, referring to the two bouncers bowled.

Shit, I'm winning this battle.

I could hear him gasping for air as he struggled his way to the crease, like an old steam train loaded with cargo as it takes off for a cross-country journey. He was going to put everything he had into this delivery. However, I'd played enough grade cricket to know that, despite all this bluster, it was going to be a slower ball. I knew that whenever I was planning on bowling a slower delivery of my own, I'd grunt aggressively at the point of delivery in a pathetic bid to confuse the batsman. It's the classic bait and switch manoeuvre.

As I'd predicted, it *was* a slower ball. It lobbed up in the air and came down on a good length, but, having anticipated this ploy, I was already in the perfect position to take control of the shot. I freed my arms and launched it long and straight, making sure to hold my follow through for several seconds. Instantly, I knew it was going the distance. It sailed long and far over the sightscreen, forming a beautiful parabola in the sky before finally coming to rest some 120 metres away.

As the bemused bowler stood there, hands on hips, I simply couldn't resist the opportunity. 'More of *that*, please!'

I watched with unabashed delight as his face fell. It was at that point I knew we would win the game.

The equation became remarkably simple from that point on. The captain slunk out of the attack and put on his opening bowlers, a desperate last-ditch effort to sneak a few wickets, but they were nothing without the new pill. Sure, young Timbo opened his shoulders (against my orders) and struck a breathtaking 38 not out off just 19 deliveries, but it was my stoic, unbeaten 31 (off 72) that truly held the innings together. We passed their total with four overs to spare.

There is nothing better than shaking hands with the opposition after a win. The winning team will always extend a firm handshake, warm left-handed backslap and extra eye contact; the losing team, to a man, will offer a limp, insincere handshake and no eye contact. Finally, I came to my opposing skipper. I grabbed his hand with confident aggression — a stark contrast to our initial greeting at the toss six hours earlier. Strangely, my hand appeared to have grown in size over the course of the day. I took his hand in mine and squeezed hard, looking him square in the eye.

'Thanks for the game, champ,' I said.

He shyly averted my gaze, mustering a timid, yet poignant, 'well batted'.

Those two simple words, 'well batted', made my heart skip a beat. It was the validation I needed. I realised that this feeling — *this exact moment* — was the reason I play cricket.

I drank 46 beers and lost my wallet that night.

THIRD GRADE MATCH REPORT
Round 10 vs. Eagles.

Round 10 had us at home against the seventh-placed Eagles, with a win vital for both teams in the race to the finals. While tensions were evident early on, Huxby No 2 has been a proverbial fortress for us this season, and we arrived at our picturesque home ground on Saturday morning full of confidence.

Yours truly won the toss and chose to bowl first on a wicket that looked like it might do a bit early. With Deeks pulling a hamstring mid-week, it was up to me to steer this ship in the right direction toward a finals berth. The main message in the dressing rooms was to work exceptionally hard, bowl in partnerships and to take our catches. If we could keep their total down to a gettable score, we'd done half the job.

Chris and Cameron took the new ball and set about completing the specific tasks that their skipper had asked of them. They looked to have the Eagles' batsmen in all sorts of trouble with their mix of full-pitched bowling and fearsome short stuff. Cameron, in particular, was outstanding and deserved much better than his eventual figures of 0-55 off 9. Many of the cover drives that went for four were airborne and just out of reach of wide mid-off or cover-point. Camo will bowl a lot worse spells for better reward, I'm sure. At one point, the plan was to bounce the cocky left-handed opening bat, so we had two men on the hook. After a few streaky sixes, we moved the deep square leg into slip and the very next ball, the ball went flying to exactly where Nathan had been fielding. It just wasn't Camo's day, but he did a sterling job for me otherwise. The left-handed opener ended up getting 80 from 52 rocks, but it was the luckiest innings I've ever seen in my life. He had no idea.

Chris, on the other hand, just keeps going from strength to strength. It's really satisfying that this club continues to churn out talented youngsters with such bright futures. From what I've seen this season, we've got the best crop of young players in the competition. It's a credit to the senior blokes at the club, who really do put in the effort to help out the young kids at training. Chris started his spell with a maiden and was excellent in the field for the rest of the day. He was unlucky not to finish with five, six or even seven wickets.

The game really seemed to drift during the middle overs. The Eagles showed a complete lack of intent. They were unable to accelerate the run-rate, mainly due to our excellent performance with the ball. Our fielding, to be fair, was absolutely amazing, too. The best I've seen it at this club. It just goes to show what a good warm up can do for a team's confidence. We hit the stump in the T-drill three times and I knew there and then that it was going to be a good day. From memory, I can only think of two dropped catches in the entire 50 overs and maybe one other misfield. Apart from that, we were absolutely astonishing. Test match standards were being set. I'll have to check the scorebook, but pretty sure Timbo kept the 'bye' tally to less than five as well, which is another sign of how he's really coming on as a wicketkeeper. He's an absolute pleasure to play with and I'm sure he's bound for higher honours.

The Eagles looked to pinch singles here and there, but the energy and enthusiasm in the 30-yard circle was too much for their ageing batsmen. We had done supremely well to keep them down to 230 on a pitch that gave no assistance to our bowlers whatsoever. We felt that a par score was around 290 and, as such, we were positively buoyant heading into the lunch break.

The run chase couldn't have started much worse, as Bretty

copped the best ball of the day — and one of the best balls I've seen this season — and was out, caught at point for a globe in the first over, which put us at 1-0. Two more quick wickets fell, and after Trav had his off-stump removed from the opening bowler with a suspect action, we were reeling at 3-14 after eight overs. Fortunately, we survived the nervy little period before the tea interval, with the captain's key wicket still intact.

Tea was absolutely immaculate. A truly great spread. Well done to all the boys for following instructions and putting on a treat for the opposition and supporters. The opposition captain didn't seem to respect the tearoom too much as he sauntered around in his spikes. Some blokes just have no respect for the game.

After tea, it was smooth sailing; one of the most clinical performances this grade has put on in some time. The running between the wickets was first class and left the Eagles looking like a bunch of absolute amateurs as they chased the ball like a dog does its tail. We brought a new level of professionalism to our game, putting away the all too frequent bad ball as their old bowlers began to tire in the heat. We were just too good for them.

A side always looks to its captain for leadership and there's nothing better for a team than when the captain is scoring runs. Yours truly chipped in with 31 not out, providing the calming influence that allowed younger guys like Timbo to hit the odd boundary as we cruised home with four overs still in the bank.

We shook some pretty flimsy hands as we walked off the field, triumphant. The team song was sung with gusto. It was disappointing that the Eagles didn't stick around for a beer — a pretty poor effort given that the game was played in good spirits.

This was the most dominant and routine victory this club has had for a while, but it's all thanks to the hard work of the players, coaches, officials and supporters. A big thanks, too, to our groundskeeper Rex. We're now only six points behind the Eagles, in ninth spot, and still a massive chance of reaching the finals.

Well done, lads ... YIEW!!!!!

Yours truly,

Skip.

7

FITTING IN AGAIN

Most grade cricketers have contemplated switching clubs at one stage or another. As humans, we have an inherent tendency to think the grass is greener on the other side. But all grass looks the same when you're standing on it for six fucking hours every Saturday, wondering what you're doing with your life. For most blokes, a club change doesn't amount to much. The only difference now is that you've got to drive an extra 25 minutes to get to training at your new club.

But sometimes, for a select few, a club switch can prove very fruitful. In many ways it's like starting at a new school, you've got the chance to reinvent yourself — not only as a cricketer, but as a person. You might have left your last club as an off-spinner who batted 8, so why not re-brand yourself as a dashing opening batsman? Your last captain sent you from fine leg to fine leg? Tell the lads you dislocated your shoulder playing footy in the off-season and — *voilà* — you're fielding in the cordon. Were you considered a 'rare unit' at your old club? With a handful of sex stories and a few lucky wins on the circuit, you could become the new Chop King. Loved and adored by all, a fresh new face for everyone to 'get around'. This social capital will come in handy the moment everyone realises that your batting is terrible, your hands are shit, and you haven't had sex since 2009.

But what's the point to all this, you might ask? Why would an ageing cricketer want to switch clubs? What is the point of starting again at a new club, toiling your way up the grades, proving yourself — both on and off the field — to a new group of sceptical blokes?

Well, I hate to admit this, but I still harboured ambitions of playing state cricket.

I could never have vocalised this dream because it would have sounded ridiculous coming out of my mouth. After all, my highest score in five years was 47 not out — in fourth grade — and I was dropped three times during that knock. I struggled to get to training *once* a week, despite being 'in between jobs'. My abdominal skinfold was so loose that I could probably have pulled it over my penis to use as a condom. There was absolutely no empirical evidence to suggest that I could ever play first grade cricket, let alone state cricket. But the dream was well and truly alive. It always is. Because for true grade cricketers, this dream is never fully out of reach. You could be a 41-year-old father of three with a BMI of 37 who bats six in fourth grade, but if you hit nine double-centuries before Christmas, you're a chance for Sheffield Shield cricket.

I switched clubs two years ago. Leading up to my decision, I was averaging well below my usual range of 13.5 to 18 runs per innings. I'd started the season in second grade, but was now barely clinging on to the number six batting position in fourth grade. The only thing keeping me in fours was our captain, a bloke called Deeks, who lived around the corner from me. Deeks' car was out of action for a few months and he needed me to give him a lift to the game every week. I was literally being selected for my ability to drive a car. At least once a week I'd have the same recurring nightmare — Deeks' car had finally passed a roadworthy test, and I'd been dropped to fifth grade. I'd wake up in a cold sweat, trembling at the mere thought of playing *fifth grade cricket,* looking around the change-room at 10 blokes, each wearing a slightly different shade of cream. God, I'm mouthing the word 'Yuck' now just thinking about it. Those were fucking dark days indeed.

My spot was in jeopardy, sure, but the club demographic was shifting, too. A new wave of young kids, fresh out of high-school, had come on board, and I'd found myself in no man's land: too old to partake in youth-focused chat about Tinder, university admission scores and Schoolies banter — and too young to chat with the older blokes about mortgages, wives, redundancies and other depressing shit. As a result, my chat became weak and repetitive. Most tellingly, my rig — once 'decent enough' — looked shameful when pitted against a bunch of first-year uni students with skinfolds in the 5-10 percent range. The only blokes with worse rigs than me were those who'd retired from the circuit a long time ago. If I had a girlfriend or a wife, then at least that'd be a reason to let myself go a bit; no one bats an eyelid when a married bloke puts on a couple of kilos. No such excuse for me: I was just a depressed comfort-eater with poor time management.

There was also one particular 'incident' that, I'll admit, did hasten my departure from the club. We were out on the circuit after our last game, a disappointing loss, which put us at 11th on the ladder. We had decided to do our traditional three-pub circuit — affectionately known as the 'golden triangle' — before possibly finishing off the night at a strip club. The strip club component would hinge heavily on whether Bruiser was kicking on or not, given that he was a) the most cashed up of us, and b) the most sexually fiendish bloke I've ever met. Bruiser was a derivatives trader at a well-known investment bank and earned an enormous salary. He worked 80-hour weeks and, as such, was unable to ever attend training, but he was a good bloke and loved splashing his cash around, so we had a safe spot reserved for him in fourth grade. Being a high-flying trader, he also knew his way around a bag of coke, but that's neither here nor there.

At the second bar, Bruiser excused himself to go to the men's room, leaving his wallet on the table. I eyed it sitting there, plump, leathery, and bulging with $50 notes.

He won't notice if I take one, will he?

I quickly scanned the room to see if anyone was watching. The coast was clear. I slipped my fingers in and nicked a crisp bill, thrusting it greedily into my back pocket.

Thank fuck. I can finally afford to fill my car up with petrol.

Bruiser never noticed that the $50 note was gone. But later that evening, Deeks sidled up to me after 12 beers. He'd seen the whole thing. He said he wouldn't tell anyone, but he was visibly disappointed in what I'd done. He banged on for 20 minutes about 'club culture', 'respecting others', and 'doing the right thing'. All this from a bloke who would, in a few hours time, gleefully cheat on his wife with a Taiwanese prostitute. This sobered me right up. I couldn't even enjoy the four lap dances that Bruiser bought for me later that night. Deeks knew that I was a thief — and Deeks was my captain! My career at this club was doomed. It'd be fifth grade for me next year, at best.

I needed a fresh start.

EMAIL

Subject: Grade Cricketer Application
To: admin@sharks.com.au
BCC: admin@settlers.com.au; admin@bears.com.au; admin@
blues.com.au ... and 40 more

Dear Sir or Madam,

I am writing to you today to announce my candidacy for the vacant
role of gun cricketer. If I can keep your attention for the next few
minutes, I'd like to introduce myself and let you know why I'd like
to play for your club.

Firstly, a bit about me. I am a top-order batsman with a wealth
of first and second grade experience. My batting technique is solid
and dependable, allowing me both the flexibility to grind out 8
off 50 balls on a sticky wicket, or provide quick runs in a chase
scenario through my innovative stroke play. I can bat anywhere
from 1-8, depending on what the team needs.

If your club is short on bowling this season, then you will be
interested to know that I am capable of bowling up to 130 *clicks*.
Given my innate ability to move the ball (both ways, mind you
— and late), I've proven myself an extremely effective weapon on
all pitches. I have five different variations of the slower ball that
I deploy depending on the scenario. I'm currently working on a
sixth one for the T20s this year.

A few years ago, having recognised the shifting demands
of the modern game, I spent an off-season learning the craft of

off-spin bowling. I undertook this extra-curricular exercise in order to have the option of switching from pace to spin mid-over, depending on the context of the game. It is now quite common for me to bowl both pace and spin during the same game. Actually, sometimes I wish I could bowl at both ends!

I am a firm believer in 'working hard' on all aspects of cricket — and that includes fielding. While many grade cricketers view fielding practice as a waste of time, something that gets in the way of a net session, I see it as critically important. I am equally at home in the cordon as I am in the outfield; my hands are safe and my arm is strong. I would add that during a game, I'll be the first person to tell a teammate to 'think about it' when his throw to the keeper hits the ground, or shoot a vicious glare at the bloke who isn't backing up. Some might consider this abrasive; I consider it to be constructive.

I mentioned the importance of 'hard work' earlier in this player application. To me, pre-season fitness is simply part of the modern game now. In years past, players would dismiss 'beep tests' and 'road runs' in the misguided belief that it had no impact on their chosen discipline, be it batting or bowling. 'I just want to hit balls,' they'd say. I would argue that this is an outdated philosophy and not reflective of the modern game. One must be fit — mentally and physically — in order to get the most out of himself. These one-percenters may not seem like much, but they are often the difference on a 42 degree day when you've got a tricky two overs to negotiate before stumps.

Finally, I would highlight my sense of humour, open-mindedness, social awareness and cordial ratios among my key interpersonal strengths. I am a team-oriented player who is always looking to improve both my own game and those around me. In conclusion, if you're looking for an experienced, selfless cricketer who will provide immeasurable value to your club, both on and off the field, then look no further.

I'd appreciate the chance to tell you more, so please do not hesitate to contact me for more information.

Cricketing and character references are available upon request.

Yours sincerely,
The Grade Cricketer

I'd sent my email to over 40 cricket clubs across most of Australia. The first nine replies were a cruel mix of bounce backs and spam. One club's auto-reply directed me to an online pharmacy specialising in Viagra. Twenty minutes later, having duly cashed in on the 50 percent discount for bulk purchase, I returned to my inbox, where I was startled to find three positive responses. All I had to do now was show up at pre-season training, see which of the three clubs was the best fit, and my state dream could live on for another season.

I showed up at pre-season training for the first club, only to find out we were doing a 12 kilometre 'time trial' road run. After about 800m, short of breath and sweating profusely, I snuck off down a laneway and walked to my car. This club wasn't for me. *No dramas, still two more clubs to choose from.*

I tried my luck at a second club the following week. As it turned out, this mob had recently hired a former state cricketer as head coach. Everyone was striving desperately to win the approval of this former state legend. As the new player, I represented a clear threat to the old blokes, but I hung around for the entire pre-season, toiling away in the nets, chatting to all the relevant power brokers to help me move up the grades. I was feeling good about my game; my fitness was improving a bit. I had even started wearing Skins.

A week before the start of the season proper, I was selected in an intra-club trial game that would ostensibly determine the teams for round one. Batting at first drop, I hit an unbeaten 88, at which point I was retired by the captain to give others a go. I sauntered off the field safe in the knowledge that I'd done enough to at least make third grade — possibly even seconds. The following Tuesday night, the selectors announced the teams for round one. I edged forward in my seat, listening intently for my name, but it was never called. I assumed that this was a simple oversight; after all, there was no way they could have looked past my excellent 88 not out, could they? I walked up to the selectors at the end of the meeting to find out what had happened. Having not been named in any of the five grades — *five!* — I asked whether they could check again to see if there had been a mistake.

'Sorry son, but it's a particularly strong group this year. We've got you on standby for fifth grade in case someone drops out,' Harold, an 81-year-old club official and eczema sufferer, politely informed me.

'But what about my glorious 88 not out?' I implored.

The words '88 not out' spat off my tongue like rapid-fire bullets. My delivery was well practiced; I'd been bragging about it all week. Surely my first score over 50 in six years had not been in vain?

'It was a good knock, sure, but there are a lot of quality *young* batsmen this year. It's a shame you're not a fast bowler — we need more of those — but there's a lot of competition in the middle order,' he said.

I looked Harold up and down, contemptuously. This was a frail, elderly man who had dedicated his entire life to the club. A stalwart who played for over 17 seasons back in the 1950s and 60s, Harold was the club's all-time leading run-scorer until last year, when Damo finally overtook him. This gentle widower was probably somebody's granddad, but at that exact moment he was the worst bloke I'd ever met.

I noticed that Harold's liver-spotted hands were now shaking, his lips quivering in fear. The poor old bastard was scared shitless; he could sense the explosion coming.

'Well, you're a fucking prick, Harold!' I stammered, crudely. 'A fucking *prick*!'

I felt my heart speed up. A surge of blood rushed to my face; my eyes began to water. It was like being at primary school all over again; a seven-year-old kid throwing a tantrum after losing his 'king' spot in handball. I stormed out of the meeting in a fit of primal rage, fully aware of the 55 blokes that were watching this drama unfold, each barely stifling their giggles. As soon as I got outside, a cacophony of laughter erupted. I had been completely ostracised by the villagers.

There's a German word, *schadenfreude*, which describes the pleasure one derives from someone else's misfortune. Grade cricket is full of fucking *schadenfreude*. In fact, the whole game centres on it. I don't think I've ever genuinely celebrated someone's hundred or five-for without considering the flow-on effect on my own position in the team. Even when I'm at the non-striker's end, I'll gently whisper 'that's plumb' to the umpire when my batting partner gets rapped on the pads. His failure is my gain. Anyway, what I'm saying is that 55 blokes took immense satisfaction in my public emasculation.

The grade cricket system is hierarchical in nature, with veterans up the top and newcomers well down the ladder. Of course, certain characteristics can help elevate one above the conventional social order — for example, a large penis and a good rig can help a newcomer leap up the grades — but for the rest of us, it's tough business starting out at a new club. It wasn't Harold's fault — he was simply the bearer of bad news. It was the fucking selection panel that had conspired against me. This club had a very traditional hierarchy, with players ranked according to power and importance. I was neither powerful, nor important. My 88 not out had presumably sparked a sense of fear among the top social strata, and as such, I was cruelly cast aside.

Still yet to find a team, and with just five days until round one, I vowed to myself that I'd try one more club before copping out and contacting a Shires team. This was definitely a last resort, though, for Shires is where grade cricketers go to die. Scoring runs in Shires feels good at the time, but you certainly don't want to tell anyone about it. Deep down you know it doesn't count. I turned up to this final Wednesday training session, just four days before the start of the season, not expecting much. The one thing working in my favour was the fact that this club had languished at the bottom of the Club Championship for the past decade. If there was anywhere I might be able to get a game, it was here.

Having been a grade cricketer for the best part of a decade, I knew that I needed to make myself known early. I approached a perma-tanned, tracksuit-clad man in his 50s, whom I took to be the club coach. He shook my hand and listened half-heartedly as I launched into my sales pitch, staring at me with dead eyes. Keen on erasing my recent past, I told him I'd just come back from a season in the UK and was looking to start fresh at a new club. I noticed that his ears visibly pricked up upon hearing the acronym 'UK'.

'What *div*?' he asked.

Unprepared for this follow-up question, I stuttered something vague about a Surrey-based competition. According to my story, I'd been paid £100 a week as their Aussie import, with board included for free. Buoyed by his sustained interest, I continued to wax lyrical about my fictitious batting average (46.7) and the swag of wickets I'd taken that season (52 — a club record). I crossed my fingers behind my back, hoping desperately that he wouldn't do a background check and find out I was a fourth grade thief with a single-digit average.

'Sounds very impressive, young man,' he said, in a fatherly tone. 'Throw your pads on and jump in the second net.'

Young man! Second net! Shit, it had been *years* since anyone had called me 'young man', or indeed asked me to hop in the second net. With this newfound confidence, I proceeded to have what I can only describe as the best net of my life. I was smoking them everywhere. The ball looked huge. For 15 minutes, I developed a temporary sixth sense, in that I knew where exactly the ball was going to pitch, every time. My brain and body were in perfect sync, for the first time in years. The bowlers became frustrated and began pitching it short, but I was too good. The loud 'clunk' sound of a perfectly middled pull shot reverberated around the indoor complex, lingering in the air for what felt like minutes. My performance was turning heads. I was actually enjoying cricket again!

Towards the end of this flawless net session, I noticed the coach beckon an athletic-looking bearded bloke over. They stood together, speaking in hushed, conspiratorial tones, gesturing towards me as I continued to pummel the bowling. I had overheard earlier that this bearded bloke was the second grade captain. Could this be happening? Was I actually being tapped for second grade? I finished the net with a confident back-foot drive (resisting the in-built urge to slog the shit out of my last one) and strolled out of the net, calmly soaking up the attention my magnificent performance had garnered. All eyes were on me, just as they had been during my hissy fit days earlier, but this time I sensed a grudging respect from those around me. *Who is this bloke? Who the fuck is this new bloke?*

As I was taking off my pads, the second grade skipper ambled over to introduce himself. Gus was his name. He was tall and swarthy, with piercing dark eyes; he smelled like stale cigarettes and sawdust. Everything about him screamed masculinity and demanded respect.

After a few casual pleasantries, Gus asked me where I usually liked to bat.

'Usually 4, Gus,' I responded, careful not to inadvertently 'champ' him.

'And do you bowl, bud?'

'Yeah, fast-meds. About 130 *clicks*,' I offered.

'Good stuff. We're playing away this week. You going to be alright getting out there?'

'No dramas, mate. Yes, I do have a car.'

My bowling was certainly not 'fast-medium'. My shoulder muscle was likely in a state of atrophy; it had been years since anyone asked me to bowl in a game. But after that net session, anything was possible. I was in-demand, hot property. My state dream was back on track.

But most importantly, I was relevant again.

8

BACKYARD SHOWDOWN

It's Christmas Day. Parents and children, friends and girlfriends, siblings and in-laws. All together, exchanging presents, sharing stories. Fresh seasonal seafood paired with crisp Chardonnay. The wine is flowing and the conversation is spirited; the sounds of chinking glasses and raucous laughter fill the air. Someone proposes a toast to the year gone — and another, to the year ahead. Then, in unspoken agreement, the party shifts to the garden for the main event. Grandpa bowls a few pies to eight-year-old Sally, does his hip. Mum's bowled for a golden duck, earns a reprieve because you 'can't get out first ball'. Aunty Josie takes a screamer in one hand, falls over, champagne glass held aloft in the other, legs akimbo. Uncle George's new wife steps in dog shit, everyone laughs, including George.

It's backyard cricket in Australia. And it's an institution.

I've already mentioned that Dad and I haven't always seen eye to eye. But as a 13-year-old, I believe I was a source of great pride for him. He came to all of my matches. He bought me *Martin Crowe's*

Batting Masterclass on VHS tape. He generally encouraged me in his own unique, unspoken way. As a cricketer, it looked like I was 'going places' — and it seemed he was on board with that.

But over the years, Dad's feeling of pride gradually dissipated. As I edged towards adulthood, he actively tried to steer me towards more academic pursuits — a gentle hint that perhaps I should be focusing my energy in the classroom rather than on the cricket pitch. He urged me to strive for a top mark at school so that I could attend university and come out the other side an eminently employable graduate with high earnings potential. Of course, I resisted his influence and chose an avenue of my own. I saw a future in cricket. Mainly, it was easier than studying or getting a real job. But while Dad had been observant enough to realise I didn't have what it would take to succeed on the field — yet not cold-hearted enough to explicitly tell me so — I was naïve. My head was swollen from all the praise I'd received as a junior, yet blind to my slowly declining batting average. As other young cricketers continued to elevate their game, I flat-lined. I had peaked at 13, and I didn't even know it.

Dad rarely asked about my cricket, even when I moved back home after living with Finn for a bit. Of course, he knew that I still played — he often gave me a lift to the train station on Saturdays so I could get to games — but he never engaged me in conversation about it. This silent protest was his way of saying, 'give up, champ'. However, my extended family still thought of me as the promising *cricketer*. I did nothing to dissuade them from this perception. At family gatherings, aunts and uncles would ask how I was going and whether I was a chance to play for Australia some day. I took great delight in telling them about my recent successes. Mediocre 20s and 30s were rounded up to 40s and 50s. I was in third grade, sure, but only due to 'internal politics' at the club. 'Oh that's too bad', they'd empathise, genuinely concerned that my talents were being ignored. Dad, meanwhile, would watch these exchanges unfold, silently judging me. I felt his eyes all over me; his sense of disappointment palpable.

One year it was our turn to host the annual family Christmas lunch. There must have been 20 or 30 people over. With my brother overseas on a Youth Leadership Summit or some shit, I naturally soaked up a lot of the attention. I pivoted all conversation towards my cricketing success, while making sure to steer the chat away from more challenging subjects that might highlight my lack of achievements away from the cricket field.

It was the end of lunch; everyone was full from turkey, seafood and potato salad; well-lubricated on premium beer and Pinot. The conversation was lively. My Mum's brother, George, spotted a cricket bat resting over by the pool fence.

'Anyone for a game of backyard cricket?' George suggested.

'I'd love to, Uncle George,' I piped up.

'No, not today you won't,' a booming voice countered, quickly.

A sudden silence ensued. I swung my head around. It was *Dad*, glass in hand, standing at the head of the table.

'Come on Dad, it's just a bit of a laugh,' I said, to nervous laughter.

'A laugh? A laugh? Cricket isn't a *laugh*, young man. There's nothing funny about cricket. It's a waste of time.'

'Just relax, darling, a little bit of family backyard cricket might be fun,' Mum whispered, in a desperate bid to diffuse a rapidly escalating situation.

Dad straightened his back, loosened his shoulders. A few seconds passed as we all waited for his next move. *What the fuck is this bloke doing?*

'OK. I tell you what,' he said calmly. 'We're going to have a game of backyard cricket. Just you and me. And I'm going to show all these people here, once and for all, that you've got no business wasting your life on this stupid game.'

I was instantly chastened. Dad had pretty much challenged me to a game of *streetball*. One-on-one. *Mano-a-mano*. The winner would walk away with everything; the loser would leave the lunch with their tail between their legs. This moment could define my relationship with Dad forever. Should I be the bigger man and decline his offer? Or should I accept the challenge, conquer my father and ascend to the throne?

'You're on, Dad,' I finally responded, through gritted teeth. Together, we rose from the table and made our way over to the pitch.

This was our family's version of *The Slap*. In Christos Tsiolkas' best-selling novel, a man slaps another couple's child at a family barbeque. The action sets off a vast chain of consequences. Each character has a stance on whether the act was right or wrong; some bound by loyalty, others on moral grounds. I wondered whether battle-lines would be drawn here, too — those on the side of Dad, those on my side — based on the outcome of this match. It had been years since Dad and I had partaken in a backyard cricket match — or any form of cricket, for that matter. Cricket had gone from being our shared interest — the thing that brought us together — to a Great Divide. I knew that Dad still loved the game of cricket, but he didn't love what it had done to me. Deep down, I suspected he blamed himself for introducing me to the sport. This was his own heavy cross to bear.

Dad flipped the bat; I called 'flats' as it spun into the air.

'It's "hills!"' he yelped excitedly. 'I'll bat.'

'Would have bowled anyway,' I muttered, reflexively.

Essentially, we would each get one innings, with the highest score crowned the winner. It was the typical backyard rules: electric wicketkeeper, one-hand-one-bounce, six-and-out over the fence. The back fence along the ground was worth four runs; any shot hit into the side of the house was awarded two runs. And in a relatively new rule that my brother and I had devised in order to keep the game moving, three consecutive misses/leaves would count as a wicket. I explained these rules to Dad as he took his position at the crease.

'Centre stump, thanks *champ*,' he ordered, out of the side of his mouth.

My Dad is champing me! My Dad has never champed me!

'Just a bit to the left ... Yep, that's centre,' I responded, slightly flustered.

Joke's on him — that's actually leg stump guard.

At the top of my mark, I realised that I hadn't bowled to Dad since the age of 15. I had forgotten his strengths and weaknesses. Was he good off his pads? Did he have a weakness against the short ball? All I could think about were the hundreds of times he'd pumped me out of the net. *Shit*, I thought. *Dad's getting inside my head already, and the game hasn't even started.*

The first ball was on a good length. Dad stepped forward confidently to pat it back down the wicket. His technique looked good, steady. I remembered that this was the bloke who taught *me* how to play. He must have been good. The second ball was a bit shorter, but

Dad was ready for it. He stepped back and across his crease, balanced, head in line with the ball. He rose into the perfect position to execute a pull shot, rolling his wrists exquisitely as he found the middle of the blade. The ball cannoned over to the side of the house. It was only worth two runs, but it was a real *statement shot.*

'Didn't even get it,' he called down the pitch to indicate that he hadn't timed the ball perfectly — even though he definitely had.

I quickly realised that I was in for a fight. For the next 15 minutes, Dad resembled a 62-year-old Matt Hayden. I had no idea where to bowl to him. Anything full, he was crunching down the ground, with the short stuff promptly dispatched to the side of the house. Dad was a big man, 6'4" and 110 kilograms, but his footwork was that of a young Dean Jones. Light, fancy. For a split moment I wondered: had he staged this whole event? Had he been secretly practicing for months, just so he could publicly humiliate me at Christmas lunch?

Frustrated and desperate, I turned to 1930s-era *Bodyline* tactics. Just as Douglas Jardine's England had done in the 1932-33 Ashes series in order to combat Don Bradman, I decided my best course of action would be to pepper Dad with short stuff. I didn't want to, but I knew it was my only option. I came in around the wicket and hurled my first delivery at Dad's body. It leapt off the grassy deck and jabbed him in the ribs. Startled, he picked the ball up and deliberately under-armed it just out of my reach.

'That's one miss,' I told him, one full octave below my normal register.

I sensed blood. In I came again, slightly faster this time, and dug another delivery into the pitch, rolling my fingers down the side of the ball upon release. This one cut in violently, striking Dad on the chest. The ball trickled back down the pitch. As I leant down to pick it up, I eyeballed him.

'That's two misses, champ. One more and you're toast.'

I looked into Dad's eyes as I picked up the ball. Now, I sensed fear. In I steamed for the third delivery. I noticed that Dad had shifted leg side, perhaps in order to combat my Bodyline tactics. However, this move had opened up all three stumps. I had given Dad a leg-stump guard anyway — despite his request for 'centre' — so he was none the wiser. The only option was to fire a yorker in at off-stump and knock his castle over.

'Got him!!!!' I screamed as the ball cannoned into the rubbish bin. Dad looked around in disbelief.

'On ya bike, *champ*,' I ordered, eyes ablaze, pointing to the imaginary pavilion.

Dad had batted well. His total of 39 was a formidable one. I hadn't scored 40 runs in a single innings in over three years in any form of cricket, so it'd be a big effort to chase it down. Nonetheless, I was confident. Dad's bowling couldn't be that good, could it? No, Dad's bowling wasn't good, but his sledging was top rate. I knew that his mind games would more than make up for his lack of guile with the ball. A 62-year-old man, he wasn't going to do me for pace. But he certainly knew how to get inside my head. He'd been doing that since I was a toddler.

In he came for his first delivery. It was short, wide, and duly punished. I leant back and cut fiercely, the side fence shaking visibly upon impact.

'What are you bowling — "right arm *help yourself*?"' I jibed down the wicket.

It was a jovial comment delivered in good spirits, designed to lighten the mood. But Dad was in no mood for jokes. The next ball surprised me. It seemed innocuous out of the hand, but skidded off the grass and kept low. I jammed my bat down just in time to keep it out.

I looked up to see that Dad was mere inches from me. It was the first time I'd seen a full-pitch follow through from a bloke bowling offies.

'You like that one, *champ*? Plenty more where that came from,' he snarled.

I looked across to the lunch table, where the rest of the family was watching with a mix of delight and horror. The atmosphere was unbearably tense. I saw Mum, head in hands, horrified at this public display of *machismo* — her son and husband, facing off against each other in a winner-takes-all fight. Next to her was Uncle George, drunk, relishing the Gladiatorial display.

'Come on Dad, knock his head off!' George slurred.

I wondered whether now was the time for a peace offering.

'Dad, maybe we should forget the score and just have a few throwdowns for old times sakes. What do you reckon?' I ventured.

He hit back with impact. 'Scared of losing are you?'

Well, obviously I was scared of losing. Fear of losing governed my entire life. But I was also concerned about the impact this match would have on my relationship with Dad. He had made his point. As a kid, Dad used to throw balls at me for hours. But as I moved into adulthood, he began to throw insults at me instead, such as 'stop wasting your time', 'get a job', and 'when are you moving out?' All I ever wanted for Christmas was a set of throwdowns from Dad. And for him to say that he loved me. This Christmas, however, he was gifting me a public humiliation.

'What's this all about, Dad?' I answered, voice wavering slightly. 'Why are we out here, doing this?'

Dad paused for a moment, sucked in a deep breath. He had calmed, visibly.

'Son, it's time you learned that, well … you're just not that good at cricket.'

I gasped involuntarily. These were the words I always feared he would say. It was one thing for Dad to silently disrespect me as a cricketer. That I could handle. But to openly tell me that I wasn't good at cricket? That fucking hurt.

'You need to *grow up*. I just wish you'd gone to university and made something of yourself. You spend all this time trying to move up the grades in a meaningless cricket competition, when you should be concentrating on getting a good job and paying off your debts.'

Obviously didn't hear about my 23 not out in fourth grade last week.

He continued. 'I checked your bank statement last week and I noticed you spent $600 at Queensgrove. What was that on?'

'I needed a new stick, Dad.'

'A new stick? Why would you go and waste your money on that?'

'I needed it. The new Grey Nicolls *Kaboom* was on special.'

It was probably the wrong time to inform Dad that I was planning on spending the rest of my Christmas bonus on a new lid and a pair of lightweight pads, despite owing my various clubs over $4000 in registration fees dating back to 2001.

'Dad, I'm just one good knock away from second grade. And once I'm there, I'm just a heartbeat away from *ones*. I'm thinking of getting a batting coach in the off-season to work on my game; honestly, I don't think it's unrealistic to think that I might even pick up a state contract in a few years time,' I said, a hint of desperation creeping in to my voice.

Dad sighed a heavy sigh. 'Mate, if you don't know now, you'll never know.'

He walked back to his bowling mark and continued to roll out a stream of insipid, flat trajectory off-breaks. But his heart wasn't in it — and to be honest, neither was mine. I settled for ones and twos in my run chase, easily accounting for the 40 run total. With the game now over, we trudged back to the lunch table.

'Who won?' the family asked, in near-unison.

'The boy won this one. Too good for the old man,' Dad announced, solemnly.

I fell into the collective embrace of my family.

'He's such a good cricketer!' an older female voice remarked.

'Best athlete in the family,' said another relative.

Someone proposed a toast: *'To cricket!'*

Uncle George wrapped his arm around me. 'Well done, legend,' he spluttered, breathing alcohol fumes all over me. I smiled politely and made a mental note to cut back on my own alcohol intake. I was just glad it was over.

Out of the corner of my eye, I noticed Dad slink away to the kitchen to fix himself a stiff drink. He slunk into the couch and flicked on the TV, cutting an achingly sad figure there in the dark, shadowy room. Weary, defeated.

I had won the game of streetball, but at what cost?

9

IS THERE MORE TO LIFE THAN CRICKET?

Having hit my mid-20s, and with little to show for it other than a rapidly declining metabolism and a blacklisting on the National Tenancy Database, I began to wonder whether there was more to life than just cricket.

I still loved the game, but was starting to feel like the game didn't love me back. I'd turn up to training at 4pm twice a week to help set the nets up, but I don't remember ever being thanked for it. Normally, I'd take delight in serving up 15 yorkers and an 'accidental' beamer to help a teammate get his eye in before an innings. Now, any bloke who asked me for throwdowns would receive a begrudging set of half-hearted, emotionally distant fullies. Even my cordial ratios were a bit off, perhaps the clearest indication that something was awry. At one drinks break, an opposition batsman actually spat out his beverage, loudly proclaiming it 'the worst fucking mix' he'd ever had. I had accidentally put too much cordial syrup in the mix, rendering it almost undrinkable. I suffered a tremendous loss of face and was immediately dismissed as chief cordial pourer.

My mind was wandering in other aspects of my game, too. For example, there's this unspoken rule in grade cricket: whenever a moderately attractive woman happens to walk past the ground, the bloke who sees her first is contractually obliged to draw the team's attention to her. In many cases, the game will halt to a standstill as both teams — including the two batsmen at the crease — stop to stare longingly at her. Only once she has passed the ground and out of eyesight can the match continue. However, I was beginning to find this simple objectification somewhat unfulfilling. I began to wonder more about her. *Who is she?* Where is she going on this beautiful summer's day? Is she off to a farmer's market to meet her friends? Maybe she's on her way to Gorman, searching for a sundress to wear to her best friend's engagement party? Inevitably, my skipper would snap me out of this daydream. 'Come on mate, where's your chat? Support the bowlers. Plenty of *talk* out here, lads!' God, I needed a girlfriend.

These thoughts were perhaps a product of the literature I was reading at the time. As a teenager, my literary diet consisted solely of cricket autobiographies. Viv Richards' *Sir Vivian: The Definitive Autobiography*; Dean Jones' *My Call*, Ian Healy's *Hands and Heals*; David Boon's *Under The Southern* Cross; Steve Waugh's countless *Tour Diaries*. I once consumed *The Bradman Albums* — two thick volumes of selected excerpts from The Don's personal scrapbook collection, each 800+ pages in length — over one rainy weekend as a 13-year-old. I was the Jeffrey Dahmer of cricket autobiographies. Insatiable.

For quite a few years after I first moved out of home, I barely read at all. The only time I read anything was on a Sunday morning, when the paper arrived. I would flick to the back pages and search for my name in the Saturday cricket results. While this technically comes under the 'non-fiction' genre, I could hardly classify this as 'reading' or 'literature'. I was just seeing whether my contribution to the match had been published; whether I was, indeed, relevant. Basically, I was just looking for any sign that I existed. It was only when I moved back in with my parents that I re-discovered the simple joy of reading. I tentatively branched out from cricket autobiographies — although I did re-read several of them, of course — and into fiction, mostly mid-twentieth century literature. I devoured everything from Burroughs to Bukowski; Faulkner to Fitzgerald. I pictured myself road-tripping America alongside Jack Kerouac, an untamed thrill-seeker with the wind in my hair and the world at my feet. In reality, the most dangerous thing I'd ever done in my life was set an 8-1 field in an U12 rep game.

Milan Kundera's *The Unbearable Lightness of Being* was also on my reading list. The book, according to scholars, is commonly seen as a challenge to Nietzsche's concept of 'eternal recurrence', posing the idea that each human life is finite, carrying with it an absence of burden, and therefore insignificant. Paradoxically, this insignificance is what weighs us down the most. I saw great parallels in Kundera's novel to my own grade cricket experience. My weighty decision to switch clubs was, upon reflection, insignificant and meaningless, yet at the time utterly unbearable. However, to remain out of duty would have given me a sense of heaviness; to depart was to pursue a path of lightness and freedom. But what did it all mean? What did anything mean? Kundera's book opened my eyes to the Unbearable Lightness of Being a Grade Cricketer.

Another book that really got me thinking was John Steinbeck's powerful 1939 work, *The Grapes of Wrath*. The Joad family makes its cross-country journey from Oklahoma to sunny, prosperous California in search of employment and a fresh start, only to encounter hardship after hardship. The labour market is saturated and migrant workers are being exploited. Meanwhile, the family, beset by tragedy, is gradually falling apart, unable to pull together in a time of crisis. The final scene in *Grapes*, where Rose of Sharon, still grieving over her stillborn child, breast-feeds a starving old man in a barn, haunted me for months. That said, I cried after reading about Dean Jones' premature retirement from test cricket. I was — and I remain — an emotionally delicate person.

Obviously, I could never tell my teammates that I was reading this *rare* literature of my own volition. The only bloke who I might have actually been able to discuss this stuff with was Tezza, but he'd recently moved interstate with his fiancée. Last I heard he was working at a big corporate, playing futsal on Tuesday nights and from all reports really embracing the 'café culture' of his new city.

Grade cricketers rarely speak of their hobbies outside of cricket. I'm sure that a lot of my teammates do take interest in things other than cricket, but I'm yet to see any evidence of this. The occasional bloke might play a bit of golf here and there, but really, that's about it. The closest thing I've ever seen to a *cerebral* hobby was when Nuggsy took up Spanish for a few months, but that's only because he was trying to chop some South American backpackers. He later tried to convince me to sign up to Salsa classes on Wednesday nights for similar reasons, but I declined the invitation. Apparently the class was 90 percent blokes, anyway.

I wasn't sure what *my* hobby would be, but I knew my life needed a bit of balance. It was certainly something that my Mum had been telling me for the past decade or so. Pinning all my hopes and dreams on cricket was something I'd grown accustomed to. Over the years, I had little to show for my time spent playing cricket, other than my friendship with Nuggsy and the sun damaged skin of a 50-year-old. But was there more to life than just cricket? Could there be anything more fulfilling than a 34 not out in third grade?

I went online and researched things I could be doing with my life. Suggested hobbies included learning a language, playing a musical instrument, woodwork, and reading. I went through these one by one, ranking them in terms of viability. A language seemed like it'd be a bit pointless. Aside from my English summer, in terms of international travel, I'd only ever been to Bali and Thailand (twice) — and I didn't need to learn a language for that. I'd always wished I'd learned the guitar, but I hated the idea of being shit for several months. As for woodwork, the only experience I'd had in this field was back as a kid, when Dad and I used to sandpaper my old V100 Slazenger after games. I'd heard reports that men who undertook woodworking had lower stress levels and an increased degree of patience. Perhaps this would be good for me. For a bloke with zero responsibilities in life other than to set the dinner table every night, I was surprisingly uptight.

Then, there was reading. Something I already loved, but had neglected for some time; something that I was *good* at. Perhaps I could join a book club, or something? I remembered a conversation I'd had once with my teammate, Starkers. He was talking about how he had to pick his missus up from book club on Tuesday nights after training. At the time, we joked about it, but now, slightly older and a bit more discerning, I thought differently.

I'd like to get into something like that.

Training was on every Tuesday and Thursday. The book club started at 7pm on Tuesdays, which meant I'd have to get away from training a bit earlier than usual. Fearful of being branded a rare unit, but nonetheless interested in pursuing a non-cricket related hobby, I told Starkers of my plan.

'You're fucking kidding me! You're joining my missus' book club? Can't wait to tell all the lads about this one!' Starkers laughed.

'Yeah, I am. But mate, you have to keep this to yourself. Sophie too. No one can ever know about this.'

'No way — this is too good.'

I had to step up my game. But what could I leverage over Starkers? All of a sudden, it came to me.

'Mate, if you don't keep quiet on this, I'll tell everyone the *real* reason you've never showered with the rest of us after a game...'

Starkers' real name was Andrew Jenkins. He joined the club six years ago as a promising 22-year-old quick, thrust into second grade, touted as a 'player of promise'. Over time, he slid imperceptibly down the grades — mirroring his own physical decline — to occupy a safe spot in fourths. Here, playing against frightened teenagers and hungover adults on drastically under-prepared pitches, his 110km/h wobblers verged on the unplayable. As a 22-year-old kid in second grade, however, Starkers was subject to a great deal of banter from his teammates. Most of this revolved around Starkers' unflinching refusal to take a post-match shower. While all his teammates looked forward to this convivial event, Starkers found it somewhat uncomfortable.

There is a great deal of pressure on everyone to have a shower after the game. But one must get *completely* naked in the shower: no half-measures. Those who wear undies (or worse, board shorts) are immediately seen as insecure and therefore weak. Here, confidence is everything. Even if one has an exceptionally small penis, he can still win the respect of others by 'owning it'. It's all about bottling your hang-ups and being 'alpha'. That last sentence is pretty much the key to succeeding in grade cricket, and western society in general.

Cricket has taught me many valuable lessons over the years: the most valuable being the need to secretly *chub up* in the cubicles before the post-match shower. It's a strange but necessary activity for all cricketers who aren't naturally 'packing'. Another popular option is to clip your pubic hair on Friday night before the game, just to get that extra 'optical inch'. They say that cricket is a game of inches. It literally is. While a few considerate players will desperately strive to maintain strict eye contact in the shower, most will unashamedly size each other up. The biggest penis will be crowned the champion — and word will carry to the selection panel.

To those who are unfamiliar with the team sport environment, this homoerotic behaviour may come as a shock. Why is penis size so relevant? Why does anyone care? *What the fuck is wrong with grade cricketers?* These are all extremely valid questions, none of which I have the answer to, yet.

Anyway, there wasn't a shred of hard evidence to suggest that Starkers had a small penis, but the implication alone would be enough. By planting the seeds of doubt in everyone's mind, Starkers could be done for. His cricket wasn't good enough to move up the grades at the moment; he was averaging around 72 runs per wicket that season. That statistic, coupled with rumours of a small penis, could send him straight to grade cricket purgatory.

My threat of blackmail hung heavily in the air.

'Mate, you know the reason I don't shower is because I have tinea,' he finally responded, voice quivering.

'Just seems a bit convenient, that's all,' I slyly countered.

'Fucking hell. Fine, I'll keep quiet on your little book club. I always suspected you were a bit of a rare unit, but a *book club*? That'll fucking do me.'

Starkers knew that in the dog-eat-dog world of grade cricket, I had his number. The grade cricket social order is subject to nineteenth century Darwinian theory: natural selection, better known as 'survival of the fittest'. Any rumour about Starkers — baseless or otherwise — would devastate his standing at the club. It's a feeling I knew all too well, having left my last club in shame after a moral indiscretion.

Having blackmailed Starkers into secrecy, I was now free to go to book club on Tuesday nights.

'What does LBW mean?' she asked out of the blue one morning.

Luckily, I had a great deal of experience in explaining the LBW law. It's actually quite surprising how many times I've been called upon to answer this question in my lifetime.

'LBW stands for Leg Before Wicket,' I started. 'The LBW rule was first invented in the late eighteenth century to prevent batsmen from blocking the wicket with their pads. According to Law 36 in "The Laws of Cricket," the ball must first pitch in line with the stumps and/or strike part of the batsman's body in line with the wickets.'

'That sounds pretty subjective. So if the batter gets hit on the pad and the umpire thinks it's going to hit the stumps, then he can give him out LBW, even if it's clearly going to miss?'

'Yes, that's right. However, the batsman may also be out LBW if, having made no attempt to hit the ball with his bat, he is struck *outside the line of off-stump* by a ball that would have gone on to hit the wickets.'

'God, how confusing!' she quipped. 'Getting a bad umpiring decision must totally ruin your day.'

I sighed. She didn't know the half of it.

Her name was Lara, like the West Indian cricketer. I'd met her at book club, where fleeting eye contact and a shared interest in Beat literature had led to a couple of dates over coffee — and soon, a relationship. On this occasion, Lara and I were at the local café, easing in to a pleasant Sunday morning brunch. I enjoyed the casual, yet intellectually stimulating conversation that we were able to have. It was certainly a change from the typical dressing-room banter. We discussed weighty topics like religion and politics; we laughed over the works of Monty Python and Ricky Gervais. There was no power struggle, no ever-present fear of being 'champed'. She didn't mock me for living with my parents like most people did. She had a significantly higher income than me, too, but that didn't seem to worry her. But most importantly, she respected the fact that Saturdays were off-limits, that I'd be spending the entire day on a cricket field, with a strong likelihood of post-match beers and circuit to follow. She didn't understand it, but she *respected* it.

'So, tell me this: why do you still play cricket?'

The question was delivered in good humour and with genuine curiosity. There was no hidden agenda; no malicious intent. But nonetheless, it disarmed me, thoroughly.

'Cricket? Well, I've always played cricket. I'm good at it, *champ*.'

Over the years I had developed a worrying tendency to apply the suffix 'champ' when speaking to my friends, family, and now Lara, too.

The responses were never favourable but it always gave me a feeling of dominance. But Lara's question had triggered a defensive reaction. Was I good at cricket? No, I wasn't. But I had been trained to hide all my insecurities under a protective alpha sheath. Grade cricket had taught me that. When threatened, one should always react with extreme aggression. A pre-emptive strike is better than a late strike. In the grade cricket world, it's *champ or be champed.*

The day before, I'd been dismissed for 24 off 89 balls in arguably the most depressing innings of my life. I must have played and missed 25 times — including one horrendous over, where a 42-year-old slow-medium bald-headed trundler beat my outside edge on six consecutive occasions. In the end, I was genuinely relieved to edge one to first slip, tuck my bat under the arm and get out of there; the sound of 11 'fuck offs' providing the soundtrack to my brisk walk to the pavilion.

A hirsute barista popped up to disturb our conversation. 'Can I start you guys off with any coffees?'

I looked at the bloke standing there, notepad in hand, exuding a casual confidence that easily matched his aesthetic. Tattooed, sinewy. The kind of guy who was definitely in a band — possibly even several bands. His wrists were adorned with colourful string bracelets, which suggested he'd spent years of his life backpacking around the world, working as a volunteer in developing nations, falling in and out of love in the most exotic of locations. Accumulating valuable life experience that cannot — and will never — be found on a cricket field. At the very least, he looked like someone who might know how to correctly pronounce the phrase 'Yosemite National Park'. He also looked like someone who might ask during a cricket match, perhaps deliberately (just to be subversive): 'which team is winning?' He looked defiantly anti-sport. *God, someone else to be threatened by.*

We made our order. I looked around the café, an old converted warehouse with just the right balance of grit and charm. The furniture was made of classic industrial materials and evoked the feeling of an old factory. Local art hung from exposed brick walls; bearded baristas grooved to the earthy sounds of Bon Iver and Fleet Foxes. I even spotted a Singer sewing machine next to the coffee machine.

Fuck me, what would Nuggsy make of this place?

The conversation continued. 'It must be great hanging out with your friends every Saturday,' Lara posed.

I stifled a snigger. *These blokes are not my friends.* They're more like my cellmates, if anything. Every Saturday, we report to jail for six hours before being sent home to our families. Grade cricket is essentially periodic detention. The communal showers are only the half of it.

It's incredible, really, the amount of pain cricketers are prepared to put themselves through. Say you're an opening batsman who gets out for a duck in the first over on day one. What compels you to hang around for the rest of the day, let alone turn up the following Saturday for day two? Yet you do, lest 10 blokes who you don't even like think slightly less of you. You retain a sense of loyalty to the club, to your teammates, even though those same teammates will not hesitate to rate your girlfriend a 'six out of 10' in front of your face. During the time I've spent watching my teammates bat after getting out cheaply, I could have learned a language by now. I could be speaking Mandarin. Instead, all I've got to show for it is a career average of 13.6 and a 10 percent discount at our local pub.

'Yeah, we have a good laugh,' I finally responded.

Minutes passed. Nursing a mild headache from the five post-match beers I'd consumed in the sheds following our 146-run loss, I flicked through the papers to check the results from the day's play, looking for my name out of habit.

'What are you looking at there?' Lara chirped, perhaps wondering what on earth I was doing in this section of the paper, squinting anxiously.

'I'm looking at the third grade results. I'm checking whether my name is in the paper,' I answered, blankly, as if this was the most obvious thing in the world.

'But you know how the team went, so what's the point of seeing the results again?'

She was right. There was literally no tangible reason for me to check the score in the paper. All the results were already online. But the sense of satisfaction one derives from seeing his name in the paper — in *print*, no less, at a time when traditional print journalism is suffering from cascading revenues and circulation — is not easily explained to a 26-year-old female with no interest or background in cricket. In fact, it's even harder to explain than the LBW law. In the paper, a terrible 24 off 89 simply appears, somewhat reductively, as just '24'. However, this lack of context looks good in print. Others reading the paper will see that I hit 24 out of a total of 164 and think to themselves, '*shit, must have been a tough deck to bat on*'. My hideous 24 suddenly takes on a new lease of life. It is no longer the worst 24 in the history of cricket; it was a stoic, brave-hearted performance against the odds. In seven years' time, the mere thought of that majestic, chanceless 24 could be the one thing that gets me through a painful divorce.

For a brief moment, I wondered whether this was what my

married teammates had to go through. I'd only been seeing Lara for a couple of months, but it was becoming abundantly clear that I'd need to keep my two worlds — 'cricket' and 'Lara' — separate from each other. Blokes like Wippa, Haynesy and Dazza (before the divorce) used to talk openly about how cricket offered them the opportunity to 'escape' from their wives — and in some cases, their children — for a few brief hours. These were blokes who were always a little too keen to stick around for a few beers after the match. Often, they had to be forced out of the change-rooms at day's end. Here, within the safe confines of grade cricket, these men were free from the domestic 'burdens' that weighed them down greatly — the same things that bring unbridled joy to millions of normal people. Grade cricket was a safe place where a grown man could happily engage in hyper-masculine banter without being branded a misogynist, or negatively influencing his own five-year-old son. Cricket offered him a valid reason to extricate himself from all familial responsibilities.

Before the marriage, the kids and the mortgage, these men had played cricket. And before they fell head over heels for Suzy, Sarah or Sophie, they fell in love with *cricket*. Once upon a time, they were all energetic 12-year-olds playing backyard cricket. They had all once achieved great success at junior level and no doubt been told by family members and club officials, on oft occasions, that they were indeed a 'player of promise'. And while they might now be 34 years of age, married, and working in a dead-end job as an assistant team manager at Officeworks, they were still able to live out these delusional dreams every Saturday. Cricket was literally a field of dreams for these desperate souls. Cricket was their first love — and boy, didn't their wives know it.

Lara was a psychologist, which explains all the questions.

Every day, people came seeking her help on all sorts of problems — depression, infidelity, drug-dependency — but she never took this negative energy home with her; an admirable trait, to absorb the troubles of others. This laidback attitude was in direct contrast to my own delicate equilibrium. If I got out twice during a net session, it'd literally take me days to get over it. Likewise, if I smashed the last ball of my net 120 metres, I'd dine out on that for weeks. Fucking *weeks*.

In book club, we'd been reading John Updike's classic American novel, *Rabbit, Run*. In this book, Updike's anti-hero Harry 'Rabbit' Angstrom is a 26-year-old former high school basketball star struggling with the demands of modern life. Stuck in a loveless marriage to a heavily pregnant wife, Rabbit flees in search of something new, a different life. He visits his old hometown in Middle America and reconnects with his school basketball coach, who reminds him how good he was as a kid. He hooks up with a prostitute for a while, seeking some form of external validation; seeking freedom from the suffocating pressures of modern masculinity.

I wondered, for a worrisome moment, whether Lara thought *I* was Rabbit Angstrom. Whether I was a 26-year-old man who had peaked at the age of 14, yet still retained misguided, narcissistic delusions of grandeur. This trained psychologist, this expert on the human condition, had absolutely no idea why I played cricket. Why I allowed my performances in an amateur competition to dictate my emotions on a week-to-week basis. Why I was comfortable sacrificing half of my entire weekend to stand on a grim-looking cricket field in desolate suburban surroundings, subject to some of the most explicit and personal abuse imaginable, when I could be doing literally anything else.

'You guys are *crazy*,' she chuckled, shaking her head in mock-disbelief. She tucked in to her smashed avocado and feta on sourdough, which had just arrived, courtesy of the cool-as-fuck waiter.

Slowly but surely, I was beginning to think she might be on to something.

10

PRE-SEASON

My emotional cycle was always the same at season's end. I'd commence a destructive appropriation of the seven stages of grieving. Hate. Relief. Peace. Restlessness. Hope. Optimism. Love. But once August arrived, I'd be ready to go through it all again.

Nuggsy suffered from more extreme bouts of these seven stages of grief, though. He revelled in the highs, pledging to get in shape over the winter, tighten up his action, work on his mental game and take on a leadership role at the club. It was part of the reason that he and I had left the club at the same time, inspired by the possibility of starting afresh. We'd come to this new club together, a dynamic duo, ready to take the grade cricket world by storm. Unfortunately, Nuggsy's lows were fucking low. It was strange that while he never punted during the season, he would always ask me for around $700 between August and September, having bombed out on several ill-advised catch-up bets. Even though I knew he'd already asked some of the other lads around the same time, I could never say no to Nuggsy. For all I know, he was running through the club earning around $10,000 and putting it on red at the casino. Unsuccessfully.

It starts with the group emails. Every winter, usually around mid-June, some bloke will send out a group email to everyone at the club to schedule the start of pre-season training. Inevitably, a small number of desperates with nothing else to do will turn up to run along a beach, or something equally romantic. A niggling competitiveness permeates throughout the ranks — and silly little competitions like 'beep tests' and beach runs only serve to exacerbate this underlying tension. I always felt slightly guilty about never going to these *pre*-pre-season sessions, but I'd often cave to the peer pressure, depending on the stage of cyclical grief I was in at the time. Of course, one's ability to run marathons means fuck all in a dressing room. If you're able to bench 150 kilograms — one single *rep* will do — you're a lot closer to playing first grade than the bloke who can run consecutive threes without gasping for breath. In the alpha world of grade cricket, chest and pipes are everything. Apologies if it seems like I'm repeating myself here, but facts are facts. If you're going to waste your time trying to improve your physique in the off-season, you need to be doing the *right kind* of exercises. David Boon, Ian Botham, Arjuna Ranatunga, Inzamam ul-Haq. You think these blokes were running on a cold and windy beach in June? No, they weren't. So why should I?

If I really wanted to improve my cricket, I'd spend the pre-season ironing out my myriad weaknesses — the short ball, in particular — rather than attend a stupid beach session in the middle of winter. If there's one thing I know, it's that 25 minutes of cardio won't stop me from averaging 16.2. I've played cricket for over 20 years of my life, yet I still cannot hit an on-drive. The short ball still causes my heart to skip a beat. Cricket is surely the only sport where you get worse, technically, with each passing year. But rather than use pre-season to work on these weaknesses and better myself as a cricketer, I prefer to take comfort in half-an-hour of throwdowns outside the off-stump. Throwdowns provide you with a temporary hit of serotonin. Essentially, they're comfort food for cricketers: incredibly moreish, but entirely lacking in nutritional value.

While pre-season training is designed to give you confidence ahead of the upcoming season, it can actually have the reverse effect. There are no turf wickets prepared because the footy season is still going, so you're forced to train on synthetic wickets. This is absolutely terrifying. Anybody can bowl a bouncer on synthetic grass. It's never a good look when the new bloke training in his whites and tennis shoes has you in all sorts of trouble with a two-piece ball that he's been shining since March. By the time the turf nets are finally ready, you've lost all faith in your own ability to hit a cricket ball. You know you've had a bad pre-season when the coach's 13-year-old son has you in all sorts in the third net with his loopy leg-spinners.

Nuggsy and I developed the term 'August hands' to describe what it's like trying to catch a ball in early spring. It's fucking cold in August, so it takes about a month or so until you can take a grab without the ball stinging your hands. The air is cold, your palms are freezing; some dead-eyed dickhead is drilling balls at your ankles, a ferocious look splashed across his face. The 'August hands' theory is also applicable when you get hit on the thigh. The hard ball skids off the synthetic wicket, striking you on the softest piece of flesh on the human body. This is pretty much the only time that I wish that I trained legs at the gym. I have no qualms splashing $120 on the 'test match quality' thigh pad, but what for? I always manage to get hit in the three-centimetre gap between my thigh pad and my actual batting pad.

Pre-season carries with it a sense of obligation. Everyone knows that if you don't turn up, you'll definitely start in a lower grade. It was the sole reason we were all there. Sure, I could have the greatest summer of my life in fourth grade. I could hit 900 runs, take 30 poles, field at first slip all day and win a premiership with my mates, but I'd still rather bat 8 and not bowl in second grade. Why, you ask? Because I want to look my friends and family in the eye and tell them that I play second grade, even if they have no idea what that actually means. Because if you think about it, second grade is just three teams away from state cricket and four teams away from being in the Ashes squad. But as the weeks roll by and the weather picks up, everyone gets excited about cricket again. The more athletic players trickle back from their rugby, Aussie Rules and soccer seasons. The groundskeepers roll out the turf training wickets; the club administrators call for outstanding registrations to be paid. I'll admit, even after all these years, nothing excites me quite like the build up to round one.

During this most recent pre-season, I was as excited as I'd ever been. My goals were set and my creams were ironed. I even washed my training shirt. In terms of selection, however, my only real goal was to avoid humiliation. Anything above fifth grade was a victory, as far as I was concerned. I was openly bullish about my chances of playing in a high grade — as I mentioned earlier, I'd learned to hide all my insecurities under an alpha sheath — but deep down I knew that anything could happen. I thought back to the time I'd hit a stunning 88 not out in a trial match, only to miss out on all five grades. I'd run out of the room in tears and never returned to the club. However, I'd learned from this experience not to take anything for granted.

As always, teams for round one were announced straight after the final Tuesday net session. We all gathered in the clubhouse for this annual event. The club had put on a special $10 'curry night' in order to wring a few extra dollars out of us; bottled beers generously discounted from $6.50 to $6.00. Five long wooden tables had been set up for us to dine at. It appeared that all the first graders — existing and prospective — were sitting together at their own unofficial table; ditto the second and third graders. A select few lower graders would be invited to dine at these tables, too, provided they were able to add value in the form of humour or chop stories. The conversation coming from these tables was loud, heavily punctuated with laughter. There was no sense of fear or apprehension. They ate and drank heartily, safe in the knowledge their grade cricket futures were secure. The remaining two tables were sparsely populated, though; it seemed as if nobody really wanted to sit there, to do so would be to admit your own shortcomings as a grade cricketer. I spied a free spot on the unofficial 'third grade table' and made an undignified beeline for it, just getting there ahead of another bloke equally unsure of his own standing. We locked eyes as I wiggled into my seat; defeated, he slowly made his way over to one of the other tables, a forlorn look on his face. There, his dinner companions would be Anand and Sanjay, two young Shires cricketers hoping to hit the big time, and Steven Hopkins, a bespectacled, pot-bellied 34-year-old bloke who'd just moved over from Adelaide on a work contract. Fucking grim.

An elderly club official had been given the task of reading the team line-ups. His voice was painstakingly slow, giving further credence to rumours that he'd suffered a significant stroke in the off-season. Regardless of his state of health, he had us in the palm of his hand. I edged forward in my seat, yearning to hear my name. I needed this more than ever. The first grade announcement came and went. Second grade, too. Suddenly, a pang of fear shot up my stomach and into my chest. It could have been the dodgy curry, but more likely, an overwhelming sense of *déjà vu*. It had happened before and now it would happen again. My grade cricket career would end here and now.

To my relief, these fears proved unfounded. I had been selected to bat 6 in third grade. Not good, but not bad, either. Average. The middle. The perfect metaphor for my middling grade cricket career. Batting 6 in third grade — the middle batting position in the middle team. Is there anything more fucking *median* than that? I didn't care, though. I'd been selected in a moderately respectable grade cricket team. Anything else was just semantics.

Two 30s and I'll be back up in second grade!

I relaxed into my chair, safe in the knowledge that I had lived to fight another day. I was still a relevant grade cricketer; I still had more to give.

Shit, I might even have a few beers and celebrate this properly.

Yes, this was going to be *my* season.

11

PLAYING AGAINST MY OLD CLUB

Returning to play after Christmas can be deflating when you're not that good at cricket. The slow wickets, the hot sun, the terrible outfields and constant confrontation with one's own mediocrity reduces cricket to a dispiriting grind. Your pre-season dreams of a breakthrough year — a year in which you achieve transcendence to reveal the star cricketer that lies within — are now a bitter memory. Every net session, every listless Saturday performance just confirms the reality that you are average. Then, Christmas rolls around and cricket takes a break. A welcome break. You see your family and friends; maybe spend some time near the ocean. You eat and you drink and it's wonderful. You return to the club refreshed in spirit but sloppy in rig, and you stagger to the end of the season, eyes deadening with every week that passes. Yes, it happens every season; only the good players score runs after Christmas.

This year, round 11 was different. I was playing against my old club. There was a spring in my step at training that week. I changed into my spikes with urgency. I did a lap and stretched before joining the nets. Excited isn't quite the word; it was more than that. Something stirred deep within me that week. It was the first time I'd ever played against my old club. *I am the centrepiece of this.* I had always striven for relevance and this fixture would catapult me there, albeit briefly. This was my testimonial, of sorts. Proactively, I decided to offer some 'inside info' to our captain regarding my old club. Still dressed in his suit, he'd placed himself at the top of the bowlers' mark in order to view our net session, where he'd no doubt get a *good optic*. It's a position typically reserved for state players, old first graders, club officials, and late-arriving captains in suits. I was some way from being any of those things, but I took my chances and slinked towards him.

I'd read somewhere that, in order to build understanding in relationships, one should employ mirroring body language. So that's what I did. The captain stood there, feet wide apart in a mock power-stance, arms folded, chewing his gum with vigour. He avoided any eye contact with me. But while his gaze was fixed on the net, he appeared to be looking beyond it, through it; as if was looking at nothing at all. This was what I had to work with, so I copied him to the best of my ability. We remained in this position, looking straight ahead, talking out of the sides of our mouths for the entire conversation.

'I know a bit about these blokes,' I started, trying desperately to mask my excitement.

'Yeah?' was his response, eyes still fixed straight ahead, arms crossed.

A ball screamed past us in the air, interrupting us briefly. Someone yelled out a belated 'Heads!' followed swiftly by the club coach wailing 'Keep it in the net!' Meanwhile, the skip was unmoved. His suit had wafts of *Joop* cologne.

'Yep. They're weak. They're really weak,' I responded. I was standing still, but inside I was rabid. I could barely contain myself.

'So, how do we go about it?' he replied, unflappable, still speaking from the side of his mouth. 'What's the strategy?'

'Mate, we have to bump them. We have to lid them …'

He must have sensed my intensity as I trailed off, because he swivelled his head 45 degrees to hold one eye on me for three long seconds. This was the most demonstrative I'd ever seen him.

'Let me get this straight,' he said matter of fact. 'Your advice is simply to bounce them.' It wasn't delivered as a question.

'Just … bounce them.'

I nodded. Immediately, I realised how stupid this sounded, but I was all in now. I couldn't back away and risk losing face.

'Cricket's a simple game,' I announced smugly.

'Can't argue with that.'

A few moments passed, allowing him to contemplate the tactics I had offered.

'Okay, I like it,' he said. 'Good thinking. Let's bump 'em.'

I was pumped. Waves of testosterone surged through me. *We will annihilate them with aggression. I will achieve redemption.* But rather than celebrate openly, I remained standing there, arms folded, chewing gum, staring blankly ahead, relishing my mini-victory.

'Cheers,' the skip said finally, which I took as my cue to exit the conversation.

As I walked away, I heard my name called out. It was the old bloke who ran training, telling me to pad up for a hit in the second net. It occurred to me that I still didn't know his name. Didn't care either.

It was the night before the match and I was restless. I took the opportunity to organise myself. I washed my whites for the first time in years, which gave me a sense of preparedness. I laid them out on my bed and stared at them for a moment. It brought back fond childhood memories of dominating the U12 club competition in clean, crisply ironed whites. Nowadays, I couldn't even pay my Mum to wash my whites for me. I put aside 30 minutes to play shots in front of the mirror. I'd defend a few balls first, before pushing a couple of balls into hypothetical gaps and whispering 'two!' I bought a bottle of Lucozade from the corner store because its branding looked athletic, and that's how I wanted to look. I'd never been better prepared for a match.

I arrived at the ground early enough to catch the elderly club volunteer dutifully removing dog droppings from the ground. He moved slowly across the grass, a metronomic air about him; he had done this before. The sun was already beating down on him as he traversed my old club's home ground with nothing but a brush, a pan, a bucket hat and dignity. No other player had arrived yet. I briefly wondered whether I should have helped him. I stayed in my car. There was no way I was going to be first to arrive.

I got out of the car once I heard the distinctive roar of cricket kit wheels rolling over rocky asphalt. Bretty, Bruiser and Chappers had car pooled, which meant at least two had deemed themselves unfit to drive. As we approached the pavilion, I realised a potentially awkward side-by-side walk was on the cards, so I held back, offered a respectful nod, and allowed them to walk past. Bretty managed a limp 'G'day, mate', while Chappers and Bruiser kept their heads down, eyes fixed to the ground. My heart was pounding. I felt odd wearing the colours of my new team, and yearned for the familiarity of my first club.

How has it come to this? Oh that's right, I stole money from Bruiser and had been shamed from ever returning.

Players returning to face their old clubs often talk about mistakenly entering the 'home' dressing room. I wondered if that would happen to me. It didn't — it just left me wondering how dumb and inattentive those other players must be. After a few minutes most of our team had arrived, except for Mitch, who was always five minutes late. Gus would normally insist Mitch buy the team a case of beer for his infraction. Mitch, of course, never did that. I always wondered why you would punish someone's disorganisation by forcing him to organise something.

I was noisier than usual in the change rooms. This was *my ground* after all. Or at least it used to be. Whatever the case, I was buzzing. I took care to ensure my warm-up lap appeared athletic, focusing on balance and driving through the hips, because I knew my old teammates were looking at me. As we passed them, my peripherals worked overtime to view their stretching circle. Bretty was holding court with what I assumed was another captivating sex story. But I sensed a hush as I bounded past; I could have sworn I heard the faint echo of that familiar word, 'yuck', just as I did at my very first grade cricket session. My stomach turned, I felt sick; I just ran faster and further away from my group.

We lost the toss and were fielding. I couldn't have been happier. In truth, I was scared about batting in this fixture. Scared of failure. Scared of being exposed as the cricketing fraud I'd always suspected myself to be. I was listed to bat at 8 but still took care to have five minutes of throwdowns, rifling every shot straight back at the thrower. I took pleasure from watching the thrower discover unfound elasticity in their legs and hips as they scrambled to avoid being struck by the ball.

Once that was done I was glad to return to the sheds. The word 'yuck' was playing over and over in my head. Were they winding me up? If they were, they'd succeeded. My fury was palpable.

'Macca bats 4,' I blared to no one in particular. 'Hates it short. Hates it at his head. Come around the wicket and bowl short at him.'

The others were minding their own business, doing the standard things like trying to finding their whites and asking for spare sunscreen. I kept going.

'Bruiser the same. Hates getting lidded. Around the wicket's the best option.'

It didn't occur to me they'd have no idea who this 'Bruiser' character was. Maybe three or four would have recognised his actual name 'M. Underwood' from MyCricket, but they didn't know Bruiser the way I knew Bruiser. I continued in this vein for another five minutes, naming every player from my old club and explaining in clipped, aggressive sentences that we needed to bounce every one of them from around the wicket.

I was in a dark place. My inner dialogue was running rampant again. *Who are these deadshits to call me 'yuck'?*

Eventually, the umpire waddled in and declared, 'On our way, boys!' in as alpha a voice as possible. *I guess you never stop trying to be alpha, even at 85*, I thought. The door of the change room opened. We filed out.

'Fuck these blokes!' I bellowed. 'Fuck these blokes!'

I had startled everyone: opposition and teammates, spectators, even the family walking around the perimeter of the oval with their dog. Birds scattered from their trees. I could hear Bretty and Bruiser giggling. Even John, my bookish former teammate, peered around the broadsheet paper he was already devouring. I kept walking, purposefully.

Yeah, fuck these blokes.

The umpires dropped the ball on the field. I sprinted out and scooped it up one-handed before turning back at my teammates, who were now a good 20 metres behind me.

'Get a lid!' I yelled. 'Get me under the lid!'

I barely knew these blokes, but I didn't care. I was going to give it to my old club. This was my time.

Our opening bowlers came over the wicket and kept a full length on off-stump, despite my pre-match outburst. I was miffed. *Why aren't they bowling bouncers from around the wicket?* There were no fireworks or incidents in these opening exchanges. The bowling was tight and the batsmen were watchful; players encouraged each other and worked hard.

It's strange to know the people playing against you, but it's also depressingly just like any other Saturday. Take their opening batsman, Jimmy, for example. I hadn't seen Jimmy since my second last game at the club, where we'd managed an unlikely victory against the top team. We roared the club song together as we stared into each other's eyes from across the dressing room. I remember the moment clearly because Jimmy was stark naked, as he often was when reciting the club song, smashing a pad against the wall to keep a percussive beat, staring directly at me. But here he was now, just another faceless grade cricket automaton trying earnestly to score runs in the early morning, and like most other opening batsmen likely to fail.

Jimmy got out just before drinks for 11. An hour or so had passed and my old club was cruising at 1-90. The sun was out, the pitch had dried out, and our bowlers were, frankly, quite shit. I'd insisted on remaining under the lid, imploring our mediocre quicks to bump the opposition, but I found their efforts insipid. So instead of yelling my instructions from bat-pad, I decided I'd run to the bowlers before the start of each over and whisper, with husky giddiness, words to the effect of: 'This bloke. Around the wicket. Chest or throat region.' Then, I'd pluck the bowler's cap off his head and jog over to the umpire, pleased to play the role of the selfless teammate.

But by now, the score had edged past 100, and I was bored. My testimonial wasn't going to plan. I decided something had to change. Our leg-spinner had just come into the attack, so I inched closer to Robbo to apply pressure under the lid.

'Come on boys, one mistake from this bloke and it's all over ...' I yelled, letting the sentence breathe for a moment before following it up with a snide remark, designed for Robbo's ears only.

'... much like you and your missus after the Thailand incident.'

I'd made the comment as our spinner was mid run-up, but to my surprise, Robbo stepped away and directed a fierce glance right at me. The game stopped, momentarily. Robbo was going through a painful divorce that I understood had many more layers to it than his indiscretions in South East Asia, but I had rattled him. Good. I was no longer bored.

The very next ball Robbo danced down the pitch and belted our spinner over mid-on, the ball careering into the fence for a one-bounce four. I laughed and clapped sarcastically. 'We've got him on the dance floor now, boys! We like seeing that!'

I had heard first graders say this stuff before. I searched vehemently for eye contact from every one of my teammates. I needed a partner, a *muse*; someone to validate my verbal tirade. Not one eye would meet me.

I responded with aggression. 'You're fucking ordinary Robbo. And you know it.' It was nasty.

To his credit, Robbo appeared to ignore me. The spinner then dropped his next ball short; Robbo rocked back and wound up for a leg-side swipe. Standing at short-leg, I did that duck-swivel thing and prayed he'd miss me. I heard the ball fizz past my ears as it screamed to the boundary. As I lay on the ground, I turned and looked up at Robbo, who stood there staring directly at me.

'Missed,' was all he said.

He kept strict eye contact with me as he (half) raised his bat in acknowledgement of his 50. There was no discernible emotion on his face; he was blank. Robbo could be a dark bloke. Last year our captain had mentioned Robbo's ex-wife in the dressing room. A week later two of his tyres were missing after training. Not deflated. Missing. No one was able to prove anything, but there was a strong suspicion that Robbo was involved.

I was starting to worry about the consequences of my actions. Obviously, I double-downed and lashed out at him. 'Don't blame me for your fuck ups, Robbo,' I blurted.

The silence was eerie. Robbo cut an imposing figure as he glared back at me. It was starting to feel like that was all he was doing in between balls. His open-necked shirt clung to his sweaty torso, dark tufts of chest hair crawling their way up the neck to glisten proudly in the sunlight. His zinc, once carefully applied, had since smeared across his face like a Jackson Pollock painting, no rhyme or reason to the pattern. Finally, he was ready to reply, and he did so with punch and poise.

'You were shit at our club. You're shit at this club. Now I'm going to hit this ball at you.'

I was stunned. At this stage I wasn't sure if I'd distracted him or fortified him. One part of me was elated that he'd risk his wicket. The other part was frightened.

The spinner dropped short, again. As I took cover, I briefly wondered whether he was doing this deliberately. Finally, I heard the crack of leather on willow.

It's actually the sound of cork isn't it? I can't hear 'leather'.

I was on the half turn when the ball cannoned into my knee, making a larger crack than the one that had sent the ball my way. I was down, writhing in pain. No one came over. I was told later the ball had still gone for four, astonishingly. I was promptly removed from short leg to the relative outpost of backward square leg. There's no status in backward square leg at all. I had been banished, exiled, vanquished. Yet another defeat in a long line of mini-defeats throughout my grade cricket life. It was all too familiar.

Lunch came and went without incident; I ate my Baker's Delight and Lucozade quietly. Towards the end of the break, I caught eyes with Bruiser and felt another wave of guilt. I wondered if he knew. He still carried around that same dead-eyed expression, so it was hard to tell.

Should I admit my thievery to him? Probably not, I concluded.

We headed back out after lunch, and it was a procession of runs. Robbo muscled the ball to all parts of the ground on his way to a very good hundred. Again, he pointed his bat directly at me in celebration. God, he had endless aggression. Unrelenting hostility. I wondered whether this was what it took to score a hundred in grade cricket. Did I require similarly deep wells of aggression in order to ton up? I wasn't sure I had it in me.

They were 1-176 now and I was disconsolate. I had tried everything to stay interested in the field. I spent a good 15 overs trying to perfect an upright seam position and shape the ball away as I mock-bowled the ball to mid-on. I went about this with more diligence than my actual fielding. The only time I switched back on was when I found myself in a footrace with our mid-on fieldsman. The one-on-one footrace is really a one-on-one battle for manhood. While I'd remained relatively quick into my late 20s, I was no chance against Frosty, a 19-year-old private school product. Frosty and I both charged after the ball after Robbo punched one through mid-wicket, but it quickly became evident he would get there first, so I used my experience to subtly file in behind him and call for the flick. 'Flick! Flick!' I cried, loud enough for the ground and its surrounds to know that this was my plan all along. The flick never came — it never really does, does it? — and even on the rare occasion it does, it seems to have no discernible bearing on the speed of the return. Frosty slid down, collected the ball, stood up and rifled it to the keeper, nearly taking my head off in the process. He didn't cast so much as a cursory glance in my direction throughout the mini-episode.

We came back out after tea to more runs. It was now about 34 degrees, with our opposition on 3-256 and ready to launch. Our legs were heavy and we were hapless; just providing the batsmen with a bowling machine experience. We had reached the stage where it felt as though a new milestone was reached every few overs. A fifty to someone here, a hundred partnership there, a club record here, a massive six there. As always, the boys were making their presence felt. An endless orchestra of 'Yiews!' echoed from the pavilion. They reserved their loudest roars for the times I misfielded, which was often.

Head bowed, I entered into yet another existential cricket crisis.

We are fucking shit. Why did I change clubs? How come this never happened when I was playing there? Why did I have to steal from Bruiser? I'm 28: why am I still playing at all? How good would the beach be? Why am I here? What am I doing with my life?

They passed 300 with ease. Aside from my association with the opposition, I was completely irrelevant. A well-prepared, confident cricketer would probably look at the situation optimistically. *This wicket will present me with a great opportunity to make a big score next week.* Instead, my thoughts were much darker. *They're definitely going to leave the covers off the deck, and we'll be stuck on a green top next Saturday, chasing 6-460 (dec).*

As usual we were behind our over rate and there was still 25 long overs to go. In the context of 96 overs of cricket, the last 25 should feel like the home stretch, but it's not at all. The last 25 overs take an eternity when you're getting pumped. Your whole team is scattered throughout the field, batsmen are milking ones and twos in between boundaries or sixes, and in my case, you're being sent from long on to long on. Another over rolled by and I was well and truly detached from this game. Detached from cricket really. My thoughts drifted to book club, to Hemingway.

What would Hemingway have made of cricket? He liked bullfighting and boxing, but English cricket was probably too posh, too considered for him. Maybe he would have liked Australian grade cricket, though? He would have lipped blokes with crisp, elegant aggression …

Our off-spinner had been brought into the attack. A 23-year-old post-graduate student, he had already been converted into a cautious, low-trajectory darter of a cricket ball — the most depressing of all crafts. I guess he was doing what he needed to do to stay in the side. We were all surviving in our own way. He instructed me to move from a long-on to a cow corner position — he must've suspected something coming — before darting another one in. Robbo, now 156 not out, got down on one knee and hauled it from well outside off stump. The ball careered in my direction, momentarily shaking me from my Hemingway thoughts. My heart was in my mouth. *Steady. Balance. Steady.* My underage representative conditioning was holding firm...

Fuck, that's well over me. Fuck, that's massive.

I sighed. Another six. I looked around just in time to see the ball disappear out of the ground. As the closest fielding player, it was my responsibility to go fetch it. But the ball hadn't lodged on a hill or open territory. This was suburbia. It had crashed on to the bitumen of the adjacent road and rolled down the driveway of a house, a nice little terrace number with a small-but-well-kept lawn.

'I think it went down that driveway, mate!' the nearby club volunteer offered. He delivered the line good naturedly, but he didn't need to be nice to me; during my time at the club I'd attempted to convey him as a shady white collar criminal from interstate who'd taken refuge in the disguise of our club's kit, which he wore disturbingly often.

'Cheers, champ,' I managed.

I was in no hurry to fetch the ball. I didn't jog with any sense of purpose. Being outside the confines of the ground was comforting, even if I was now essentially a man walking through leafy suburbia in dirty white clothes and Oakley sunglasses purchased in 1994, which made me look like a speed dealer.

I wandered away from the ground towards the house, searching for a cricket ball that symbolised my cricketing life: battered and lost. I made my way down the paved driveway and was drawn to the house alongside it. It was painted baby blue; its lurching shadow offered brief respite from the 34 degrees of sun that had been annihilating me all day. I realised I was alone. Save for the rough sound of my spikes scratching against the concrete, I was now experiencing a sense of calmness and serenity. Specks of light danced between the leaves of a jacaranda tree that towered proudly over the house. A light breeze blew gently across my face and I permitted myself to close my eyes and enjoy it for just a moment.

As I was reflecting on the length of this driveway, I spotted a gate swing open about 20 metres in the distance. Two people stood there — a guy and a girl, both roughly my age — waving in my direction. I looked at them for a moment before continuing on. I resumed my search for the shredded cricket ball, no doubt lodged harshly within some non-descript bush, all chewed up, leather hanging off it like skin after a bike fall, before stopping in my tracks. I looked back at the two people, who were now calling out to me. I made my way over to suss the situation out.

'G'day mate,' the guy said.

It was friendly. I was on guard.

'We're in here.'

I walked in, initially unsure of why I had been beckoned. Those thoughts drifted away as I set my senses on the picture before me. A lush, green, spacious backyard. An infinity pool. Thirty young adults and a fifty-fifty gender split. Unthreatening melodic indie music hummed softly from bespoke speakers. There were people scattered throughout the yard; some in groups, others locked in personal conversations. People were laughing. I saw dozens of women dressed in gorgeous summer dresses. A couple of guys were over in the corner jamming on acoustic guitars, but not in a pretentious manner.

Where am I?

'G'day buddy,' one of the guys said. He seemed to be the host, but there was no alpha about him.

'H ... Hey,' I stammered.

I didn't know what to do. I was unaccustomed to such raw friendliness. My eyes darted back and forth as I tried quickly to compute this tranquil scene. Bright colours danced around me. I saw manicured beards, craft beers, and — again — sundresses. Yellows, reds, blues. I felt the noise of the party soften and eyes narrow upon me. The rest of the party had twigged that a sunburnt man dressed head-to-toe in cricket whites was now amongst them. The sounds of Vance Joy faded in the background.

They're all looking at me now.

I gathered myself. My chest tightened. I went for it. 'I guess I didn't get the memo for the dress code,' I tried.

There were laughs. Actual laughs, even from the girls. Where there weren't laughs there were smiles. Was this an ad? I didn't care, I felt great.

The crowd returned to their conversations. This had been a momentary amusement to them. They picked up where they left off; back to their lively discussions about books, movies, gigs, comedy. Something to do with art, probably.

The host approached me. 'Mate, are you looking for this?' he asked, brandishing the battered cricket ball in one hand.

I cocked an eyebrow. *What was* he *doing with the ball?*

He picked up the social cue and assuaged me. 'We saw you hunting around outside so we presumed you'd lost the ball. A couple of us dug around and found it under the table here. It's hot out there and it looked like you could use a break, so we invited you in to chill for a bit.'

I *could* use a break. But was it that obvious? It probably was. I didn't have time to overthink his comment, though, because the next thing he said floored me.

'So ... which one do you want?' he quipped, presenting a full, kind, and earnest smile.

He faced me with both arms outstretched. In one hand was the cricket ball. It was so withered it was no longer 'red'; more a fading grey colour. It had aged terribly. It had lost life, each over like another year — another year closer to death. It had lived 81 overs, most of it in despair. In his other hand, though, was a freshly opened beer. For me. Premium. Ice particles gracefully sliding off the bottle. Clean, modern branding. I couldn't think clearly. The host knew my dilemma, but was relishing it. He eyed me mischievously. I was struggling to rationalise his offer.

'It's a beautiful day, mate. Enjoy a quick beer,' he said.

It was a beautiful day. How long had I been gone, though? Three minutes? 20 minutes? This had felt like forever. I couldn't have a beer, surely not? This was *grade cricket*. Grade cricket was the 'best amateur competition in the world', so they said. I'd happily have 14 schooners before and after the match, but during the match was unheard of. Then again, this was such an idyllic scene. Was this what life on Saturdays was like? An endless stream of daytime barbecues with nice people and strong gender ratios? How bloody compelling. But

I surely couldn't just drink beer while everyone at the ground was waiting for me. Others would surely be looking for the ball by now. They would find me here soon enough.

My mind went into overdrive. I wondered if they'd recommenced the game without me. *Can they even do that? Would they even notice I'd gone? Would I really reject the most perfectly presented beer in my life? What life is this? And even if they did notice me, what difference would a beer make? If I have to bat tonight, would a blood alcohol concentration of 0.007 make any difference to my 8 off 32 deliveries?*

'Hand me the beer,' I said finally.

I grabbed the beer and drank it heartily. I talked with the host and his girlfriend Erin — who wore a yellow sundress — for four minutes. We discussed whether Triple J had become too commercial in recent years, all of us settling on the affirmative. I nodded at everything that was said. I felt good, at peace. Then it was time to go. I quickly said my goodbyes and made my way to the gate.

'Don't forget the ball, mate,' the host shouted, to several cheers.

I turned around sheepishly and flashed a smile. *Shit, I'd nearly forgotten the ball!* Of course I had; I'd chosen the beer. The host underarmed it awkwardly to me. Normally, I'd have made a wise crack, but I was so buoyed by this experience that I bypassed those tired thoughts. He didn't need to be coordinated. His underarm found me nonetheless. I caught the ball nonchalantly, closed the gate and strolled down the driveway toward the ground, ball in hand. At the top of the driveway I swivelled, sighed and took one last look the house.

One day I'll host a barbecue like that.

Almost immediately, I became enveloped with terror. The

ground was now in full view, and I'd been gone for what seemed like 15 minutes. Maybe 30. Had the game recommenced? I couldn't remember anyone spending so long looking for a lost ball. *Fuck, I've gone AWOL here*, I thought, immediately returning to the crass inner dialogue that plagued me when consumed with cricket matters. As the other players emerged in my eye line I broke into a jog, feigning urgency. My anxiety was alleviated when I saw that play had not recommenced. Still, I knew a rebuke was coming — likely something along the lines of 'Where the fuck have you been?' I had tasked myself with finding a stray cricket ball and ended up partying, so it was a fair question.

As I jogged purposefully to the boundary, I stopped dead in my tracks, since it was clear there was no need for urgency. Players were scattered about the ground, most of them lying down. Those that weren't horizontal were sitting down, heads gently bowed. A few had registered that I'd returned with the ball, but it didn't trigger any serious response. It looked like the fucking apocalypse had arrived. Out on the centre wicket, I noticed two players standing there with Steery, taking it in turns to hold his bat, no doubt enquiring as to its imperial units of measurement. 'This 2'10 or 2'11? Feels like 2'10.' Yes, they'd be saying something like that.

'Oh, you're back,' Lenny said. 'Wish you'd taken a bit longer. It's nicer lying down.'

There was no irony in his voice. It became apparent that nothing at the ground had changed. Another ball had disappeared, and then reappeared. I, on the other hand, had gone somewhere else — a place that would leave an indelible mark on me. A place of warmth and happiness. A place that provided a looking glass into my future. And just as quickly, I had been violently shaken back into this desolate reality. I wasn't even sure what was worse: the depressing scene itself, or that I'd voluntarily walked back into it.

My old club ended up hitting 374. We trudged off the field, broken. We had four overs to negotiate before stumps.

We finished the day 2-6.

I was a nervous wreck in the days leading up to week two of the match, with texts flying in from my old club mates. There wasn't much variety to the messages; in fact they all said the same thing: 'Quack.' I had to hand it to them, they had batted as a team last Saturday, and now, even in abuse they were unified and on-message. It occurred to me that I'd developed a grudging admiration for the unity and ruthlessness of my old side. How could I not see this when I played there? Maybe I was the problem? I counted 31 text messages with the singular word 'Quack' in it that week. It was legitimate harassment, but at least they weren't saying 'Yuck'.

I was listed to bat at number 8, but with two wickets lost overnight I was essentially a middle order player, which buoyed me. I arrived at the ground sharp and purposeful; I felt fresh as I wheeled my bag into the away dressing room. I warmed up solidly, relishing my early invitation to hit balls during the extended throwdowns session, pumping at least 40 balls off the middle for others to field. I was in the zone, so I declined all requests to deliver throwdowns myself or to field balls for others. They talk about taking ownership in cricket: I was taking ownership today. This was my day. I had a job to do, and I wasn't here to deliver throwdowns.

We started promisingly enough, reaching 2-35 after about 10

overs. I started to feel confident we could match it with my old team. Maybe not win the match, but not be completely embarrassed either. Sure, 2-35 isn't a wonderful score, but it contains within it a modicum of respect. It says, 'Yes, we've made some mistakes, but we do have the capability to score runs consecutively.' I was allowing the relief to slowly wash over me when Choppy nicked a good one, taken smartly by Bruiser diving behind the keeper at first slip. At 3-35, we were in trouble again.

Fuck, that was a good dismissal. This cricket is good. I don't know if I'm this good.

I went to pad up, which I always did when there were three wickets to get before batting. This action would always prompt the same unimaginative utterance from every grade cricket robot. 'Why are you getting padded up so early, mate? Don't you trust us?' I'd normally respond with something like 'just hate rushing', but the truth was that I experienced weekly nightmares about getting timed out. I couldn't risk that happening in real life.

Four down soon became five down, and I was in next. The opposition were bowling really well. 'Oohs' and 'Aahs' rippled across the ground every over. Our middle order was struggling to combat this sustained pressure. The ball was moving around indiscriminately: flying past the outside edge; jagging back in and rapping batsmen on the inner thigh; rearing off a length through to the 'keeper at head-height. The cries of anguish were soon replaced with laughter, which was even worse. Teams start laughing when they know they're going to win. We were 5-60 chasing 374. Our number 7 stick, Mitch, was utterly hapless, and before long he spooned one to short cover — I mean, actually *spooned* it, as if to say 'I don't want to be here. This humiliation is too much. Here, have this.' Bruiser took the catch with such nonchalance that it intensified the electrical current of fear and nerves zapping through my body. Mitch was out. I was in.

I've got a pretty good routine for walking into bat. I copied it off a bloke called Sam, who was in my U12 rep cricket team. He scored a couple of 50s here and there so I considered him elite. My gloves would be resting in my helmet as I sat there waiting to bat. Following the dismissal, I'd remain seated, count silently to ten, calmly remove my strapped gloves from my helmet, fix my helmet first, then my gloves, and emerge zen-like on to the field. At the gate (if there was one) I would increase my walk to a gallop, whereupon I'd play three decisive shadow strokes: all straight drives. I'd follow it with a few twists of the torso, and walk purposefully in the remaining 15 or so metres to the wicket.

However, this time I fumbled my gloves and helmet, causing the helmet to make a shattering noise as it crashed on the hard, yellowing concrete of the pavilion. Since the opposition was beyond even needing to celebrate, the ground was already in near silence. I flung out a hand in a desperate attempt to catch the falling helmet on the second attempt, but this only made it worse. The vigour of my grasping attempt was such that I managed to strike the helmet and impart more force than it already had, sending it bouncing along the concreted pavilion surface. It left me flustered and shaking, with everyone else looking at me, including the players on the field. I walked briskly over to the helmet and flung it on as quickly as I could, narrowly avoiding tripping over a sewerage vent as I galloped onto the field.

'Here he is, boys!'

Now all 11 pairs of eyes were on me as I approached the striker's end. My batting partner, Devvo, had made the unfathomable decision to meet me at the edge of the square. I couldn't quite hear what he was saying, but I think it was something along the lines of, 'They've been waiting for you mate. They won't stop talking about you. Just *work hard.*' Even though I'd walked straight past him in clear rejection of his protection, I was ridiculed anyway.

'This is fucking village. Is this under 11's?' Robbo said.

'Are you going to retire on 30? Fuck *me,*' Bruiser scoffed.

I desperately wanted to tell them that the meeting wasn't my idea; that I wasn't village; that I agreed with them, maybe even that I wanted to be on their team. I didn't, though. I just asked the umpire for two legs.

'Yes, that's two legs,' he replied swiftly.

Thank God, at least I've done something right.

Coming into bat can be strange, especially when you're a lower-order batsman. You've been watching the show from a distance, about 80 metres away, where everything feels benign. There's a bowler, a batsman, fieldsmen, umpires, and the game. It's all very straight-laced and pure from the pavilion. Fieldsmen are the quiet little pawns on the game's chessboard. But when you finally arrive on the stage, you realise there's much more to it. The previously anonymous opposition suddenly reveals its personality. They're now alive — chatting about things, chipping away at your psyche. Every delivery has more meaning, every movement you make is scrutinised. It can be overwhelming.

By now, some darker clouds had started to circle. The wind whipped through my grill as some new kid glided in, swinging ball after ball past my bat. I sternly admonished myself in a bid to elevate my game. *Concentrate! Watch the ball! Stop looking at his face at the moment of delivery!* My feet barely moved as I swished again. Finally, I jammed my bat down on a yorker, squeezing the ball down to fine leg off the inside edge, and I was off the mark. Relief.

'Great shot, Trippy,' Robbo said, making reference to an obscure fourth grader we'd once played with.

Trippy had been a top order batsman with an impeccable technique. The problem was that he never scored runs. Trippy's impeccable technique was a source of derision at the club. He looked brilliant against ball machines, but just could not middle a ball for the life of him. I felt sorry for Trippy, because he was a great bloke who tried hard. Sadly for him though, the result of his approach was a litany of balls that rolled gently to mid off and cover. The opposition feigned hand and finger injuries upon fielding his shots, mocking his lack of power. At the end of the day, grade cricketers want to be physically powerful, nonchalant and alpha. I later learned that Trippy had left the club to become a bodybuilder, and quite a successful one at that.

I battled on. At first it was weird facing blokes I'd trained, played, circuited and gambled with. I had left the club in secret shame and had never resolved it. I wondered whether Deeks had told anyone. I looked out to point and there he was: arms folded, leaning slightly back, feet in a wide power stance like a Crows Town nightclub bouncer — a picture of anger, repression, intimidation. He wore dark sunglasses so I couldn't establish true eye contact, but the fact he shook his head every time I looked his way gave the impression he hadn't forgotten the incident.

I had now survived ten overs, and had even struck a boundary, albeit behind square. The opposition was unperturbed. Despite my growing partnership with Devvo, they retained three slips and a gully. *If I can manage ten overs here I can manage anything*, I told myself. Already I had conquered my greatest fear: that I would be humiliatingly dismissed within a few balls and exposed as the fraudulent cricketer I am, devoid of talent, skill and character. I was mixing it with these guys today. *Maybe I can actually play?* These thoughts cycled through my mind as I clipped one to the left of mid-wicket and came back for two. *I'm in here*. I thought. *Work hard*.

Then, I was promptly hit on the pad and given out.

My old mates told me to 'fuck off' as I walked from the field. And just like that, it was over. After 50 minutes of intense concentration, wrestling with myself mentally, I was out. Just another batsman dismissed for *not much* in a staggering collapse. My meagre total just another contribution to the status quo. Cricket is too often like that.

Having removed my gear, I sidled up to the scorer to check what we were on. I did this to appear interested in our team's progress; really, I was just scanning for my name and personal tally. I had made 8 off 32 balls. 'Felt high', I volunteered to my nearby teammates, who were staring blankly out onto the field. No one made eye contact with me, but I wanted some acknowledgement. I wanted to cast some doubt on the validity of my dismissal. There was nothing, just silence.

Finally, Butch met my gaze. He stood, turned to me and sighed. 'Hitting all three mate', he said, before bowing his head and walking straight past me to go on a solitary lap of the ground.

Another wicket then fell; more ironic 'yiews' ensued. Half an hour later, we were all out for 124, with 25 overs still left in the day.

'Put 'em on mate, you're batting 4,' the skipper said, in between sips of his Red Bull energy drink.

It was a grim situation. We were trying to stave off an outright loss and the top order batsmen — including our skipper — didn't want to bat. I was nervous, but of course padded up as instructed. Within ten overs, I was making my way to the crease. Thankfully, I didn't drop my helmet this time.

The atmosphere was completely different to what it was in the first innings. There was no sting to the opposition's comments; they were just mucking around. Despite the cordial atmosphere, I still played and missed at my first ball, much to everyone's enjoyment. I saw out the over nervously, fully cognisant that one more single-figure score would drag my season average down to below 12.

The game was petering out when I cracked a few incongruous cover drives to the boundary, taking me to 20. All of a sudden I was 'in'. That the boundaries came from the bowling of the wicketkeeper was inconsequential, for I was making runs now. Robbo had bowled about five overs in his decade-long career. He laughed when I swiped him over mid-on for four. The next ball, I took him the distance, pumping his full toss over mid-wicket. Deeks called a halt to play before the ball had even bounced, as if to say 'this *was* funny, but it's starting to depress me now'. I was 33 not out.

We had been comprehensively defeated, but I was privately elated, riding the high of my unbeaten 33. Of course, all grade cricketers are well practiced in disguising their elation, and I was no different. I put on my best disconsolate face and offered the limpest of limp handshakes to the opposition. They in turn complied with the protocol, each player looking over my shoulder while whispering something resembling the words 'good game'. Everyone except for

Deano, of course, who made good eye contact and offered an insincere sentiment like 'good luck for the season,' or something. He always did this, and it made him appear like a strong bloke in the opposition's eyes. He was a terrible bloke in real life, but this was his thing.

I made the familiar beeline for the change room, mindful to amble slowly and without purpose. This was the walk of the defeated; they must appear as though they're in some sort of daze, wandering aimlessly, inconsolable for at least 50 seconds. I maintained my hangdog expression as my thoughts oscillated between my exemplary 33 not out and where I would drink that night. It was then that the coarse sounds of 11 bellowing men boomed through to our dressing room, as our opposition commenced their team song. My old team song. It was always incumbent on some *coat* to say 'never forget this feeling boys', and on this instance, Butch duly obliged. It was even more common for someone to make a disparaging remark on the tune itself, as though poor melodic and lyrical composition somehow provided comfort to a losing side. Anyway, the song brought old memories flooding back. Nuggsy talking to me at training and taking me for a beer. My first win for the club. My first tub at the club. The night I stole $50 from Bruiser's wallet. I'd started daydreaming, because the next thing I knew someone was talking to me, trying to grab my attention.

'What are you doing, mate?' Gobbler said.

'What are you talking about?' I shot back. I had scored 33 not out, so I had status.

'You're humming the song next door.'

'Oh … didn't realise.'

Jesus. Had no idea I was doing that. It's a good beat, to be fair.

Most of the team had scattered pretty quickly afterwards, which tends to happen after a major loss. Some of the younger kids skipped away without having a shower, which I promptly chastised them for. As our dressing room thinned out, I could hear my old club next door, laughing it up, yelling, yiewing. I couldn't shake the need to speak with Bruiser, and whether it was the 33 not out, or something deeper, I felt emboldened. I sprang up and headed into the opposition change room, nervous, but with purpose. I took a six-pack as collateral, held my breath, and entered.

'Here he is, boys!'

I stood in the doorway, incongruous in team colours only, and was welcomed immediately. The boys were laughing and happy to see me. They were rapturous.

'You blokes are a terrible *unit*!' roared Timbo, who had consumed two post-cricket beers, thus rendering him intoxicated.

'It's great to see you mate!' offered Robbo, the bloke who only 45 minutes earlier had intimated that I didn't belong anywhere near the same field as him; and one week prior, had been deliberately hitting balls at my head, with the intention to cause grievous bodily harm.

Everyone was warm and cordial, and keen to see how I was doing, on and off the field. I felt welcome and at home. I made my way to Bruiser after a few beers. He'd just emerged from the shower, so with only a beer in hand and a towel around his considerable waist, we stood in the corner of the dressing room together. He'd made 56 batting at 5 and taken a great grab at first slip: the perfect performance for a wealthy 34-year-old in third grade. We engaged in a little bit of small talk: I told him about my girlfriend and, after another beer or two, how I'd joined a book club. I eventually worked up the courage to make my confession.

'Bruiser I have to tell you something,' I started. 'Last year, on our end of season circuit, at the strippers ...'

Bruiser sensed something was coming; I didn't normally sound so serious when talking about the strippers.

'... I made a really stupid, drunken decision, and ... I stole fifty dollars from your wallet,' I blurted.

Bruiser nodded. He looked calm, so I continued on.

'It was just sitting there, and I convinced myself — ridiculously — that you didn't really need it. So I took one. Anyway, Deeks saw me and absolutely gave it to me. I was so ashamed. That's why I left the club. I'm so sorry.'

I decided to wait for Bruiser to react now. I had just emptied it out; I had been talking too much. I wondered if I was about to ruin not just his mood, but that of the entire dressing room.

After what seemed like an age, Bruiser spoke.

'What'd you spend it on?' His eyes were lively and a broad smirk broke over his face.

'Um ... to be honest mate, probably just the cab home, maybe a coffee the next day and a sandwich? I don't really know,' I replied. I hadn't expected that question.

'It's a hell of a confession, mate,' Bruiser chuckled. 'Takes some balls to come in here and tell me that.'

I remained silent.

'Listen, don't worry about it. You're right, I do have plenty of $50 notes. The only mistake you made was stealing one, because I'd probably have just given it to you anyway ...'

Relief surged through me.

'... But I really respect that you've fronted up and told me, and

I'm sorry you felt the need to leave the club over it.'

'I thought it was my only option,' I responded.

'Look, what's done is done. We always enjoyed having you around. The boys were also saying how much they've enjoyed playing against you too. They were having a great time watching you sledge Robbo — he hated it. We loved it, because as you know Robbo is a *cunt*.' He'd said the last part of that sentence loud enough for the whole dressing room to hear. Everybody laughed, including Robbo.

'I'm really happy to hear things are going well with you. You've got a girlfriend, you're reading widely, and you're playing second grade. It's tough to balance your personal life and creative pursuits with a career as an amateur cricketer. And to come and apologise to me shows a ton of character. Well done.'

Bruiser paused briefly before asking the inevitable. 'Now, are you going to come out on the circuit with us tonight?'

'Of course he is!' chimed Robbo.

Of course I was.

12

THE FINAL CHAPTER

For professional athletes, the decision to retire is never taken lightly. Perhaps arthritis of the knee has set in, or chronic back issues have become too much to bear. Some quit before they suffer the ignominy of being dropped; a proud decision commonly known as retiring on your 'own terms'. This tactic enables them to bow out to great fanfare while maintaining their legacy. And many simply wish to spend more time with their family. The life of a professional cricketer involves a lot of travel; many lonely nights separated from your loved ones. It's a bittersweet experience listening to little Madeline's first words via Skype when you're on a meaningless two-test tour of Pakistan in the UAE. Understandably, you'd rather be there in person to share these precious moments.

Sadly, the amateur cricketer has no such excuses. For him or her, it is a stark, confronting realisation that this simply cannot go on any longer. The constant failures have become mentally fatiguing. The risk/reward of spending your valuable weekends on a cricket field just isn't paying off. Unfortunately, there's nothing idealistic or romantic about retiring from your club team. Rarely will tears be shed. In many ways, it's a relief — for all concerned. *Thank fuck, it's finally over.*

For amateur athletes — particularly middling grade cricketers such as myself — retirement can be an even tougher, more agonising prospect than it is for our professional counterparts. There's no job in the Channel Nine commentary box to look forward to; no seamless transition into paid coaching. There's no testimonial match at the SCG featuring a host of former players and current radio/TV personalities. No publishers clamouring for the rights to your tell-all autobiography. None of that stuff.

Cricket wasn't keeping me from my family, or cutting into my work hours. I was a childless man with a terrible job — still am — and in many ways, cricket was what defined me. I wasn't suffering from any injuries either; I wasn't athletic enough to get 'injured'. But in recent years, as this book attests, the game had worn me down. Every single Saturday morning during cricket season, since perhaps the age of 25, I'd woken from my bed with a sinking feeling in my gut. I was sick of the politics. I was sick of the failures. I was sick of having to act alpha, when I was naturally a beta male.

I can still vividly recall my first century. I was 12, batting in a representative fixture, edging closer and closer to an unlikely and unprecedented milestone. Finally, the moment arrived; I nudged one behind square and set off for the single that would mark my coming of age. I waited for the team to start clapping, to roar my name from the stands, but nothing came. It seemed I was the only person who had even realised I was on 100, having diligently counted my runs throughout the entire innings. But as is often the case at amateur level, a belated applause burst from the pavilion at the end of the over. I raised my bat triumphantly, turning to salute each corner of the ground — even though the 20 or so spectators were all congregated in one specific area — savouring my childhood heroics. And there, in the distance, I saw Dad, standing and clapping slowly, a faint smile offsetting his typically emotionless face. God, the pure pride I felt at that moment — I've never felt anything like that since. But would I ever get to feel like that again? Would Dad ever be proud of me again? At this point, it all seemed very unlikely.

In recent months, I'd made peace with the idea of never scoring a grade cricket century. I'd talked it over with my mates — with Nuggsy, with Finn, even with Lara — and they'd assured me that it didn't reflect who I was as a person. My inability to conquer the grade cricket scene had grated on me for all these years, but I was learning to let go. In truth, the backyard cricket match I had with Dad over Christmas lunch — that infamous *streetball* clash — some years ago now, had a real effect on me. Since then, I had begun to engage in new extra-curricular activities, which were giving me great joy. Not just the book club — which had reinvigorated my latent interest in literature — but other simple pleasures, like camping down the coast with Finn and some of my other non-cricket mates, like going to music and comedy festivals with Lara and her friends. Discovering the joys of a Saturday brunch. I'd even enrolled in a couple of 'charity fun runs' — a bold new step for me, but one that had enabled me to feel like I was helping the community. Basically, I was becoming a more rounded individual — and I wasn't sure whether I even had time for cricket anymore.

It was late March, the last game of the season. I'd been dropped to fourth grade to give some young kid a go in thirds. He was a 'player of promise' — *there's that fucking phrase again* — and I was the dispensable older player, the ageing Hollywood actress to his young, emerging starlet with undeniable box office appeal. The selectors diplomatically claimed that they were just 'playing around with the teams', but I knew this was a mortal body blow. Next year, I would certainly start in fourth grade. Perhaps even in *fives*. I shuddered at the thought of batting in the third net, or sharing a weathered pill with a fifth-grade leg-spinner. I hadn't been in the third net since the early 2000s. It'd be like flying economy after years of first class travel.

The game was being played about 30 minutes from home. Our opposition, the Dragons, sat handsomely in second place on the ladder, assured of semi-finals cricket. These were the worst kind of games. I turned up at the ground to meet my new teammates, most of whom I'd never spoken to before. I was slightly late, having never played at this grizzly venue before — a No. 2 ground in the middle of nowhere — and the lads were already warming up. I slung my kit down in the corner, having shoved someone else's kit aside to get the prime position, and took a second to reflect on the year gone by.

Hmm, another great season. Got sledged every weekend of the summer, dropped nine catches, and my car broke down twice. I did score one 30-odd, though, so I guess it hasn't been a complete write-off.

During this solitary moment of contemplation, I sniffed the dressing room air. The grades may change, but the smells remain the same. Most adult cricketers fail to wash their whites during the week. As such, the stench of crusty, unwashed cricket whites dominates all dressing rooms, from first grade down to the lowest level of park cricket. These filthy, grass-stained clothes have been stewing in their cricket kits all week, resting against sweat-laden cricket pads, leaky sunscreens and perhaps even a long-forgotten banana peel — itself having languished there for months, all mouldy and brown. As the day goes on, assorted chemical fumes — cigarette smoke, Dencorub and Aerosol —will add to this powerful mix. This here is the true scent of grade cricket. An offensive aroma, yet one strangely comforting in its familiarity. Having breathed in the air of male failure, I slowly ambled out to join the others on the field.

Getting dropped is a big blow to the ego. One day you turn up to training and she tells you its over. Even though you saw it coming, it's still always a surprise. I guess the one good thing about it is that you're 'back in the game' a week later, getting to know 10 new blokes. I joined the group and stood there, arms crossed. I silently cursed myself for forgetting to bring a sweater. The March air had a crisp autumnal chill to it; cold dew sheathed the grass. If not for the constant sound of massive airplanes whooshing overhead — we were stationed right next to an airport for this fixture — I could have sworn I was in England again.

Fourth grade wasn't a chance for the finals this year. From experience, these last few games before the end of the regular season were the grimmest of all. The warm-ups become increasingly half-hearted: there are fewer hits in the T-drill, the throwdowns have less venom, and well, no one gives a shit. I was keen to get this game over and done with and crack on with the post-match beers. The final season's circuit was historically one of the most notorious.

'Just eight hours until we can get out of here and *can on*,' I announced crudely, expecting some murmurs of approval.

I got nothing in return. To my surprise, I noticed a difference with this team. There was a strange, positive energy, a real focus, a sense of purpose. It wasn't what I expected from a fourth grade outfit with nothing to play for. The body language was good, confident.

Everyone was wearing their correct training uniform — right down to the club-issued socks.

'Still a game to win here, mate. We can finish the season in 11th if we get up, which will do a lot for club championship points,' said a bloke whom I knew to be 'Bubba'.

Bubba's retort earned some positive cheers from the rest of the team; my comment in comparison seemed flippant and ridiculous. My only encounter with Bubba to date had been in a pre-season trial match, where he sternly instructed me to 'work hard' from his position at first slip. Bubba was 40 kilograms overweight, unemployed, and still lived with his 82-year-old mother, which made me wonder whether he was qualified to extoll the virtues of 'working hard'. Nonetheless, given his superior age and body mass, Bubba appeared to be the alpha male in this pack of young broncos. I had no business turning up and subverting the team culture with such a frat boy remark, anyway.

I looked around at my new fourth grade teammates. Limbering up against the fence was Jordie, our 16-year-old opening bowler and designated player of promise. He had one of those awful asymmetrical haircuts that are becoming increasingly ubiquitous among the younger players. He also boasted a labret ring, listened to the local alternative radio station and attended all-ages indie gigs in his spare time. I wondered whether I should tell him to conceal this alternative side in order to progress up the grades, but thought better of it.

To the left of Jordie, gingerly stretching out a hamstring, was a bloke called 'Lloydy'. I didn't know much about his cricket, but I did know that he was the official fourth grade Chop King. I'd seen him out drinking beers with some of the first grade lads after training. I'd even chinked glasses with him once or twice and stood in on some of his stories, laughing at his punchlines. As I would soon find out, Lloydy wasn't a good cricketer at all — in fact, he wasn't even a fifth grader, to be honest. He was diabolically shit. Normally, a player of that standard would be running around in Shires cricket, B Grade 'seniors', or some other competition where the men wear baker's whites and keep their shirts deliberately untucked in order to hide their unsightly abdomens. But Lloydy himself was far from a sore sight. His thick, wavy chestnut brown hair sat marvellously underneath his baggy cricket cap. His eyes were like glistening blue infinity pools; you just wanted to grab a cocktail and lay in them for hours, watching the sun settle over the horizon. His storytelling was rich, both in content and delivery, giving light to otherwise dull grade cricket fixtures and training sessions. I looked forward to feasting off these tales in the cordon, assuming I would be fielding there alongside him. I'd pat him on the back after yet another dropped catch; he'd look back at me, dimpled ho-hum grin — 'aw, shucks' — all would be forgiven in an instant.

Of course, there was Nuggsy, too. Good old Nuggsy, who had stuck with me all these years. We'd been dropped for this match together, as if we were a package deal: he, the grizzled, charismatic club veteran; me, the former child prodigy who never amounted to anything, the Macaulay Culkin of grade cricket. He'd been there during my lowest points — the stealing incident with Deeks; the embarrassing night out at Lounge Bar with Finn — and the good times, too. We'd circuited together on the night I finally lost my virginity. He brought a second pair of gloves out to me that day I hit 37 not out in a trial game. All the great moments. And I hoped that perhaps he'd be by my side for my next moment of glory, whenever that might be.

Then there was our captain, Chooka. Patrick 'Chooka' Cook was a lovely bespectacled 36-year-old man. He had a gentle, fatherly demeanour and wise, knowing eyes. His torso was soft and pillowy — as far from a hardened 'rig' as it comes — yet he seemed to have no body image hang-ups whatsoever. He treated his potbelly as a badge of honour; the result of a life well lived. He'd spent a lot of time in the south of France, where he had developed a special affinity for soft cheeses and crisp aromatic white wine. I'd heard that he'd often bring such delectable treats for afternoon tea during home games. This humble man was the perfect choice as fourth grade captain.

Sadly, I'd overheard many of the young, top grade players heap shit on Chooka behind his back during the season. They mocked him for being slightly pudgy and past his prime. They took him on simple face value, as was the grade cricket custom. Some of them even went a step further, implying sinister motives for his continuation at the club. Because after all, why would anyone bother putting his hand up to captain fourth grade? It means you'll never get promoted up the grades. You're essentially signing your own grade cricket death certificate.

A few months earlier, I was at the pub with a couple of second grade teammates after training. About six of us were there, standing erect with beers in hand and chests out, trading vastly exaggerated sex stories like Bitcoin. Generally speaking, it was unusual for the lower graders to join in on these exclusive post-training gatherings, with the exception of Lloydy, who was welcome anywhere on the basis that his mere presence might attract a few women. But on this occasion, Chooka had wandered in with a couple of the young lads in fourth grade, including a 19-year-old Indian bloke named Vikram dressed in full whites. We strived unsuccessfully to avoid eye contact with them.

'Hi, boys,' Chooka offered upon approach. 'How's second grade looking this weekend?'

'Yeah good, champ,' someone responded, curtly.

'Oh that's good. I hear you boys are an outside chance for finals this season. Plenty of runs to be scored at Hislop Oval this weekend!'

One particularly noxious bloke named Marty Henson saw this as his cue. 'Sorry, champ, but what *grade* are you in?'

Chooka, a former second grade captain, had skippered fourth grade for the past six years running, steering them to two premierships in that time. He was an institution at the club and adored by all the junior players. His ability to broker positive relations with the umpires had single-handedly ensured we didn't finish last in the Spirit of Cricket awards. Put simply, he'd done more for the club than anyone at this little gathering had ever done for any institution. But, to his detriment, Chooka was a balding 36-year-old man with a mediocre rig and an unspectacular sexual history, so no one at this little gathering really cared too much about Chooka.

'Just fourth grade, mate. Love the game though!'

Henson smirked. A villainous smile crept upon his shit-eating face. 'Seriously, champ. You should just fucking *give up*,' he sniped, with alarming hostility.

The group went silent, save for a couple of apprehensive whistles from the lads. God, Henson was a horrible fuckwit. *But would Chooka rise to the challenge?*

Instead, Chooka just laughed. 'You're probably right, Marty! I could never match it with you young blokes in second grade.'

And with that, Chooka cheerily made his way over to the bar with the young fourth grade lads to shout a round of well-earned drinks.

'Old Chooka just loves hanging around the *young boys*, doesn't he?' Marty called out. 'Fucking *paedo*.'

To my eternal discredit, I never said anything.

I've sat through hundreds of pre-game speeches from all sorts of captains. Usually, the message revolved around 'working hard'. Whatever you do, make sure you do it *hard*. Deeks and Gus — the two captains under whom I'd played most of my adult cricket — were both strong adherents to this generic maxim. But in this pre-game briefing, I was shocked to find a completely different tone. In his address, Chooka covered several different themes. It was a rich, engaging talk about passion, discipline, honour, integrity and pride. Pride in the club. Pride in your teammates. But most importantly, pride in *yourselves*. It was more of a TEDtalk than a fire-up speech. It was also a refreshing change to see a captain wearing pants while delivering the pre-game speech.

Having called for quiet, Chooka kicked his speech off by introducing an interactive element. 'Look around the room, lads. Have a look at the blokes around you. I know that a lot of you don't know each other. Fourth grade can be a bit like that. You've got young kids coming up from fifth grade, and good players who've hit a rough trot and have found themselves in fours. So just take a second to look at the bloke next to you, shake his hand, and introduce yourself to him.'

A few seconds passed before anyone moved.

'Go on, introduce yourselves!' Chooka urged.

I looked at the bloke next to me — a young kid, couldn't have been more than 18. I put my hand out and introduced myself. I kept it brief, offering just my name, age and batting position.

'Oh, nice to meet you, mate,' he replied. 'My name is Aaron

Tompkins. I'm 18 and just moved here from the country. I bowl seamers and bat a bit.'

Aaron seemed like a lovely kid. He had disarmingly large hands for an 18-year-old, and his accent was broad and friendly, like all good country lads. He was young, naïve. I wondered whether this naiveté would change after tonight's post-match circuit, where he would likely be exposed to the twin horrors of grade cricket — adultery and alcoholism. But at this moment, I saw nothing but hope in his eyes, so I humoured him.

'Oh you've just moved here from the country? You'll love it here, mate. Grade cricket is the highest level of amateur cricket in the world.'

I had unwittingly echoed the very same words that Nuggsy said to me at the bar all those years ago. *Grade cricket: the highest level of amateur cricket in the world!* It was the first time I'd rolled out this phrase to a fellow player. I'd been hearing such statements for years, so they must be true, surely? We *were* the best amateur cricketers in the world, weren't we? *Weren't we?* Perhaps one day I would expand on this chat. I'd explain the feudal system in grade cricket. I'd drive home the need to work on his rig (it was sloppy), memorise Will Ferrell quotes and establish a mystique around the number of women he had slept with. But I'd save that for another time.

A minute of polite chat passed, before Chooka continued his address.

'As you can see, lads, the wicket is a little bit green, but I've chosen to bat first because I believe in our top order. I believe that we can get through the new ball and prosper. But, of course, it's going to take some *character* to do that. The former US president, Abraham Lincoln, once said that character is like a tree, and reputation merely its shadow. Character, lads. It doesn't matter whether you've averaged less than 12 with the bat this year. What matters to the success of this team, today, is whether you are all willing to display *character*.'

Fuck me. This is rare.

'Finally, the most important thing we need to remember today is to enjoy ourselves. That's the reason we all play cricket, isn't it? To do what we love? We wouldn't spend half our weekend doing something that we hated, would we? So to the top order batsmen — make sure you get through the early swinging ball and cash in on those loose ones. There are plenty of runs to be scored on this deck, but dig in early. Character, lads. I want to see *character*.'

And with that, Chooka calmly read out the batting order and returned to his seat. His speech had roused a fire deep inside me, inside all of us. I felt inspired, but not in a basic, animalistic way. The usual basic response to 'work hard' was to go out and try and blow the opposition off the park with a torrent of bouncers, sledging and white noise. But Chooka's approach was more considered; more cerebral: the perfect blend of pop psychology and blokey real-talk. It was all about *character*.

As our openers made their way out onto the field, I grabbed Chooka for a quick moment. 'Mate, that was a great speech. I'd never heard that quote by Lincoln on character,' I whispered.

'Thanks, bud. I try to weave in these references in order to achieve cut-through with the guys. I know what it's like listening to the same pre-game speech every time.'

'Oh, you mean like the classic: "let's just work hard and get these cunts out"?' I posited.

'Actually, I prefer the Latin translation: *Labor omnia vincit*. Anyway, good luck out there today, mate. I'm sure you'll get a big one today. But don't take this team for granted. They're better than your average fourth grade side.'

I took a deep breath and chucked my pads on. I was batting three today. First drop, just like Bradman.

Labor omnia vincit. Labor omnia vincit. Work fucking hard.

I secured a plastic Ikea chair next to Jordie, placed my gloves inside my helmet, and turned my attention to the game. The ball was moving around a bit, it seemed, but our openers were holding firm. I looked around at my new teammates, seated all together, eyes glued to the match. There was a sense of togetherness that I hadn't experienced in years. Everyone was genuinely hoping for a good start. No one was secretly praying for a teammate to get out in order to boost his own chances of not getting dropped.

Once the first few overs had been safely negotiated, things relaxed a bit, and everyone settled into their usual practices. I was seated next to Jordie, who was telling everyone about the rare vinyl copy of *My Bloody Valentine's* seminal 1991 album, *Loveless*, he'd bought for $5 at Vinnies, earning some light-hearted banter from Bubba — 'How fucking *emo* are you, mate?' — and the rest of the lads. A few seats over, Lloydy whipped out his smartphone and, to the delight of Nuggsy and several other blokes, began furiously swiping away on Tinder, a public show of virility. It was only 10.30am, but Lloydy already had 16 matches. Bubba flicked through the newspaper, legs crossed and reading glasses on, a study of deep concentration. Bubba was brushing up on that afternoon's race schedule at Rosehill Gardens. Meanwhile, our skipper, Chooka, had taken on scoring duties for the first 10 overs, and was making pleasant conversation with the opposition scorer (a young player's mother) about falling property prices in the district, which had apparently been brought on by a recent proposal to expand the nearby airport.

Suddenly, a wicket fell. I composed myself, picked up my lid and bat, and strode purposefully to the crease to the encouragement of my teammates. 'Come on, mate. A big one from you today!' someone yelled.

Yeah, a big one from me today. That sounds good.

A few overs passed and I was feeling good at the crease, striking up a good rapport with my batting partner, Jacko. Just as I'd warmed into my innings, a new bowler came on. His name was M. Peterson. I knew that because their skipper yelled it out to our scorer when he came on to bowl, as is the custom. However, it soon became apparent that M. Peterson's nickname was 'Tickets'. As he limbered up to bowl, I heard 10 blokes urge 'Tickets' to have the spell of his life.

'Come on Tickets!

'Your man, Tickets!'

'This is your day, Tickets!'

It wasn't the first time I'd come across someone named Tickets. It's actually quite a common nickname among amateur Australian sportsmen. There's something beautifully simple and predictable about grade cricket nicknames. Those stockily built players are given the moniker 'Nugget'. My 'Nugget' was the sole exception to this law, on the basis that his actual name was 'Alan Nugget'. Someone with a strong sense of self-belief will usually have the name 'Tickets' bestowed upon them, as this bloke did, to indicate that he has purchased 'tickets' on himself, such is his confidence. On a similar tangent, one bloke I played with had the nickname 'Bridgestone' — a reference to the old Bridgestone Tires slogan: *'Bridgestone: That's Confidence'*. This was narrowed to either 'Bridgey' or 'Stoney' whenever he was bowling. He was an absolute nightmare of a bloke — arrogant as fuck — but the 'Bridgestone' nickname was our affectionate way of telling him so. Naturally, all 'Daves' are nicknamed 'Danger' — an abbreviated version of 'Dangerous Dave' — just as all Rods are automatically known as 'Rocket'. Those new to the club are generally just referred to by their initials (*i.e. 'great fielding, JP'*) until further notice. At one club I played at, there were three blokes called Nugget and four blokes called Tickets. Needless to say it got a bit confusing at times.

Anyway, Tickets was about 34 and tall, with long scraggly hair, scrawny arms and a sparse, wispy beard. He had an eyebrow ring that probably looked good on him in 1996, but now gave the impression he was battling a meth addiction. Whatever Tickets had to be cocky about, it certainly wasn't his rig — he bore a frightening resemblance to Christian Bale in *The Machinist*. In short, Tickets was your quintessential first-change grade bowler: reasonably sharp, but nonetheless a loose unit and not accurate enough to be trusted with the new ball.

Once the encouragement had subsided, Tickets came in for his first ball. It *was* sharp and beat me for pace. Clearly, Tickets had played a bit of first or second grade at some stage, probably before the ice addiction. I looked at the pitch to give others the impression that the ball had done something off the deck, even through it had held its line entirely.

'Too sharp for him, Tickets!'

'*That's some serious heat from you, Tickets!*'

'*Doesn't want to be here, Tickets!*'

Tickets surged in again, all arms and legs. Again, the ball was full — but this time it moved off the deck, violently so. I had absolutely 'no fucking idea' — and the fielders knew it, too.

'*Great wheels, Tickets!*'

'*Playing with the big boys now, Tickets!*'

'*He doesn't want to be here, Tickets!*'

I needed to show Tickets who was boss, lest he purchase even more tickets on himself. I couldn't let some upstart fourth grade meth head embarrass me. I was a third grader, after all. Shit, I'd even played a couple of seasons of second grade.

They're just playing around with the teams, I reminded myself, *just like the club selectors said. You'll be back in third grade next season, where you belong.*

In Tickets came for his third ball — and again, he did me all ends up. I lunged unsuccessfully at a ball wide outside off-stump, drawing groans from the expectant cordon.

'*All ends up, Tickets!*'

'*Backing you, Tickets!*'

'*Doesn't want to be here, Tickets!*'

That last comment — 'he doesn't want to be here' — frustrated me the most. It was the third time they'd used it in that over. I fucking hated that phrase (probably because it was true). So, against my better judgment, I quickly turned around and blurted to the cordon:

'Guys, I *do* want to be here! I really do want to be here today!'

It was the worst thing I could have done. The cordon collapsed into a collective fit of giggles. It took them two minutes to recover. I shot a quick glance at the square leg umpire. Even he was having a wry chuckle. An 82-year-old umpire, giggling at me. It was a new low.

Tickets wanted blood now, and so did his 10-strong cohort. Normally, three consecutive misses in grade cricket leads to a wicket. It's practically a *fait accompli*. Lower grade cricketers, in particular, lack the *character* required to dig in at these tense moments. But character was something that Chooka had urged us to demonstrate at all costs. Therefore, I would dig my heels in and see this prick out.

Tickets launched into his stride — an ugly looking mixed action — and planted his back foot on the crease. Unfortunately, for Tickets, his legs got tangled up at the point of impact, and he hit the pitch with a loud thud that belied his 60-kilogram frame, crumpling to the ground in a scraggly, unkempt heap. He let out a tremendous groan similar to that made by a distressed cow standing in line at the abattoir. It was a truly haunting sound.

Jacko and I hurried over to see how the bloke was, to discover a rather grizzly sight. It was immediately evident that Tickets had suffered a compound fracture. A bone — his fibula, I believe — was protruding so far out of his leg that its outline was visible through his whites. He would probably never play cricket again. Lucky bastard. I'd like to say that I had some sympathetic thoughts for Tickets. After all, he was probably going to relapse back into drug dependency upon his first hit of morphine at the hospital, undoing years of hard work. But deep inside, I was absolutely elated.

Thank fuck Tickets is out of the attack.

With Tickets gone, some middling part-time off-spinner was called upon to complete the over. I peeled six runs off those three balls. I was starting to feel good, starting to feel that this could be *my day*.

How quickly the game can change.

I'd batted with Nuggsy many times during my career. Once, just a few years back, we'd shared a match-winning 100-run partnership in third grade. Another time, in my debut season as a 19-year-old, I ran him out after calling 'yes' on a late cut that went straight to gully. He chucked my bat and pads in the urinal later that day out of spite, but we were stronger mates for the experience. But this time, we were both undeniably in the twilight of our respective careers. Both in fourth grade, together, for the first time.

Nuggsy came in when we were about 4-120. I was batting well, on about 30 or so, and therefore the 'senior' partner. However, Nuggsy was a natural aggressor — regardless of the situation. After three plays and misses in his first three balls against their opening bowler, who had come back on for his second spell, I wandered down the wicket to have a quiet word.

'Mate, maybe you should just see this bowler out. I reckon he's only got one or two overs in him before he fades out of the attack. Once he's gone, we can really punish the part-timers,' I reasoned.

'Mate, I'm not here to *fuck spiders*,' Nuggsy shot back, angrily. His nostrils flared alarmingly as he uttered the uncouth phrase, like a rabid wildebeest.

Nuggsy was not one for temperance. In all facets of life, short-term satisfaction took precedence over long-term outcomes. He didn't have home Wi-Fi because he could never stay on hold long enough to speak to a customer service representative. He'd never held down a job for more than two years. All his relationships — with the exception of his failed marriage — had fizzled out before the six-week mark. Asking Nuggsy to simply 'see out' the bowling was like advising Jordan Belfort to invest in safe, long-term, low-yield stocks. After all, Nuggsy was not here to *fuck spiders* — and he never would be.

Nuggsy was bowled next ball attempting a slog sweep to a yorker on off-stump. At the point of impact, his head was literally facing the sky above, like a toddler gazing up at the birthday balloon that had escaped his grasp. Without even turning around to inspect his shattered stumps, he bellowed the word 'FUCK' (which sounded more like 'fark') at the top of his voice, the 'FAAAA' sound reverberating around the park like a bushman's cooee.

'Pack em, champ!' the bowler ordered, pointing in the direction of the pavilion.

Nuggsy eyeballed him for a fleeting moment, as if quickly computing the repercussions of belting the guy — *'I'd be suspended, the police would be involved, it'd be a whole thing … yeah, I better not'* — before reluctantly complying with the directive. I watched with a mixture of apprehension and delight as Nuggsy marched towards the sheds with never-before-seen intensity, a fearsome look upon his face. Out of the corner of my eye, I spied four teammates quickly slip into the sheds, presumably keen on getting good seats for Nuggsy's meltdown. To be fair, his post-dismissal tantrums were legendary. Once, he broke seven dressing room windows after getting a first-baller in a second grade semi. Our club manager, who'd fought in Korea, later described the aftermath as 'a fucking war zone'. Shards of glass all over the floor, in people's kits, and in the middle of it all was Nuggsy, head down, hands bloodied from the violent outburst, like a man who'd committed a terrible crime of passion, just waiting for the cops to arrive and take him away. *Oh my God. What have I done?* He never paid the club back for the damage, mind you.

Out came the new bloke. Darryl, a doughy 28-year-old, had recently been promoted from fifth grade. He was wearing a floppy brimmed hat and mismatched baker's whites. I somehow swallowed the urge to tell him it was 'fucking village' to come to the crease looking like a 60-year-old Greek gardener. As was often the case, I settled for a simple 'Yuck' under my breath.

Some 30 minutes passed, and Darryl and I were striking up a nice little partnership. He was incredibly talkative between overs; a thoroughly engaging conversationalist. During our time in the middle, we discussed a wide range of issues, ranging from the immediate onshore threat of Islamic State militants to the possible whereabouts of the original girl from the old AAMI TV ads. Darryl had an opinion on everything and, frankly, it was a joy to converse with him.

At the end of one particularly lively mid-wicket conversation, I said to Darryl, 'Gee you can talk, mate. Are you in sales, or something?'

Darryl laughed. 'Actually, I am mate. I've been working at this listed IT company for a while now. They treat us really well and I'm actually in line for a senior role. A bunch of us are off to Hawaii in a couple of weeks to mark the end of the UK financial year. It's basically just a huge piss-up for 10 days. Can't wait!'

'That sounds awesome, mate. I've been working in insurance tele-sales for a while, but it's pretty dry,' I lamented.

'Mate, we might actually have a job if you're interested?' he replied, with alacrity.

My ears immediately pricked up. Yes, I was interested. Very interested.

'What kind of role is it, Darryl? I'd really like the opportunity to handle "real" clients.'

'This is pretty much a regional sales manager gig — you'd be covering the Victoria and Tasmania territories, selling software solutions B2B. There's a strong business development aspect to it as well, so there'd be a fair bit of opportunity to travel. We're listed on the NASDAQ, so there's the chance to move to the US down the track if that's something you might consider. Could be a really good move for you, actually. I'll chat to my boss about it on Monday and we'll see if we can line you up an interview or something. We need to fill the position pretty quickly, though.'

'Shit, thanks mate! So what kind of on-target earnings can I expect?'

'Well, the base is pretty decent — about $80,000 — and if you hit all your monthly targets, you can get up to around $140,000. Joycey cleared $150,000 in his first year last FY, and he's only 26. The company has some tough KPIs, but they're all designed to get you to hit your targets. But the "product" is so good it sells itself. It's a great environment and there are some cracking blokes within the sales force — I think you'd like it.'

Fuck, $80k. That's more than double what I'm on.

I suddenly realised that Darryl and I had been talking for five minutes. The umpires were already in position. All 11 fielders had started screaming at us. 'Any danger of a game of cricket?' the bowler barked angrily from his mark, hands on hips.

'Fuck, sorry lads!' Darryl and I apologised in virtual unison.

I rushed to my crease to take strike against the bald, 30-something bowler. For some reason, I was 70 percent more scared when facing a bald bowler. I'm not sure why the absence of hair makes a cricketer more fearsome, but it truly does. Even as he approached the wicket, all heavy breaths and front on chest, my mind was somewhere else. I was picturing myself living in New York on $140,000. I'd live in a loft apartment on the Lower East Side; attend Knicks games at Madison Square Garden. I'd jog through Central Park on my lunch break and shop at Trader Joe's. On weekends, I'd venture over to Brooklyn and browse a flea market; drink Pabst and catch an indie gig in Williamsburg. Maybe Lara could come with me? There were plenty of neurotic people in Manhattan, based on the Woody Allen movies I'd seen, so I'm sure she'd be able to find a job ...

Stop thinking about Darryl's job offer, and concentrate on the ball, you fucking idiot. Work hard! Labor omnia vincit!

By now, Darryl and I had been at the crease together for about an hour or so. We'd put on a partnership of about 80, and I'd been enjoying myself so much that I'd stopped counting my runs. I had entered a cosmic state; I had rhythm and energy to my batting, for the first time in years.

Without warning, the drinks break arrived. God, it had been so long since I'd been batting at drinks, I'd forgotten what to do. I glanced over at Darryl, who had taken off his gloves, placed them on the pitch along with his bat, and walked over to the boundary's edge. I quickly followed suit. Out came Nuggsy and Lloydy with the water bottles — Lloydy resplendent in club tracksuit, not a hair out of place, looking a million bucks; Nuggsy in shorts, bare feet and a tattered blue wife-beater singlet which positively screamed 'Centrelink'. Nuggsy took two glasses over to the umpires, while Lloydy serviced the rest of us with effortless charm, refilling glasses on request. Darryl and I took a glass from the drinks tray and toasted to our partnership. We enjoyed the well-earned brew. Nothing beats an ice-cold glass of Cottee's cordial.

After buttering the umpires up for a couple of minutes, Nuggsy ambled back over to Darryl and I. He looked around carefully before lowering his voice into a quiet whisper, addressing me directly.

'Mate, do you want to know?' he asked, coyly.

'Do I want to know what, Nug?' I responded.

'Do you want to know what you're *on*?'

Nuggsy was rarely coy about anything. I knew all sorts of personal things about Nuggsy. I knew whom he voted for (Tony Abbott — because he's a 'strong leader' and said he'd 'stop the boats'); I knew the age he'd lost his virginity (15, to a distant relative). I was also aware that he'd spent three nights in a Bolivian jail after being mistaken for a mysterious, high-level cocaine distributor — because he used his one allotted phone call to brag about it to me. Nuggsy was an open book. But for Nuggsy to act this way, so strangely aloof, something was obviously up. I must have been close to three figures.

Sometimes it's better not to know what you're on. Nerves can set in and you start batting differently. The pragmatic, left side of the brain takes over; the free-flowing slam poetry shelved for a dour, conservative approach. But when it comes to runs, you need to know. Sure, the element of surprise is lovely in many cases, even liberating. Like when your partner is expecting and you both agree to keep the sex of the baby a surprise. Or when you find something special under the tree for Christmas, something that you hadn't expected. But with runs, you *need* to know what you are on so that you can prepare yourself for the moment you reach that milestone. So you can turn to the pavilion and salute, just like I did that day as a 12-year-old. Anyone who says they 'don't want to know' is a fucking liar.

After a fleeting second or two, I turned to Nuggsy. 'Mate, I want to know. I *need* to know what I am on.'

Nuggsy cocked a knowing eye at me.

'Mate …' he said, pausing for dramatic effect. 'You're on 97.'

Fuck! Oh my fucking god!

I had been Mr Casual up until this point, but Nuggsy's information was a game-changer. Now, I was ruled by fear and anxiety. Familiar emotions, to be fair.

But Nuggsy wasn't done yet. 'When you were on about 60, I sensed you were a chance for 100. So I made a few phone calls. Look over there,' he gesticulated to the grassy knoll.

I swung my head around. I saw a young slender man, dressed in cool contemporary clothing and a straw hat. He looked like a folk musician — bearded face and languid posture: an incongruous sight at a suburban cricket ground. Of course, it was Finn. He waved earnestly. I tipped my bat back in acknowledgement, somewhat bemused. Next to Finn was a young woman. It was Lara, my Lara. She'd never been to a single game of mine (I had strictly forbade her from attending matches), but Nuggsy — *good old Nuggsy!* — had convinced her to come and be a part of history. There she stood on the grassy knoll, next to my best non-cricket friend, wearing a yellow sundress that danced in the breeze, a vision of femininity. She, too, waved, her other hand shielding her eyes from the sun. I felt a knot in my heart. *This must be what love feels like.* Love felt strangely similar to the feeling I got from striking the perfect cover drive.

'Um, there's one other bloke here, too,' Nuggsy added.

I was perplexed. I didn't know anyone else who'd voluntarily attend one of my cricket games. My mate Tezza used to come to a few after he retired from grade cricket, but he was living the corporate life in a city far away, so it couldn't have been Tezza. Then, I saw him. A tall, heavy-set moustachioed man, probably in his 50s or 60s, standing behind a tree, partially obscured. He was wearing a black golf hat — the same one popularised by Greg Norman in the 1990s — and thick-rimmed aviator sunglasses.

It was Dad.

I instantly fell into a state of panic; it felt as if my nervous system was about to shut down. A cold sweat trickled down my brow; my heart rate accelerated rapidly. *Dad's here.* But why? *Why* was he here? What on earth was he doing at this suburban cricket ground? Did this mean he still cared? Was this my chance to finally win his approval? Or had he come for more macabre reasons, in the hope that I would fall agonisingly short of a ton? Had he come here to taunt me for a life wasted? To tell me that I'd left the oven on again?

I needed to get this hundred.

Word had got around the opposition that I was closing in on the milestone. The captain had brought his strike bowlers back on. The field was up, with two slips and a short cover now in play. The chat had returned — *'he doesn't want to be here'* — and the fielders were on their toes. Only this time, I truly *did* want to be here. I did want to get this hundred — and nothing was going to stop me.

I'd safely negotiated the first five balls after drinks. On the final ball of the over, I was presented with a half volley outside off-stump. I pushed at it eagerly and called an urgent 'YES'. Startled, Darryl took an eternity to heed my call. He had every right to be startled — the ball went straight to short cover. But I had set off running — and

Darryl had no option but to comply. The fielder picked it up cleanly and returned it to the keeper with minimum fuss, and Darryl was caught eight yards short of his crease, out for 49. As he walked off, I avoided eye contact, and hoped dearly that his job offer would still be on the cards come Monday.

In came Lloydy, with the score at 6-200. Lloydy batted eight and didn't bowl, but he was sometimes good for a quick 20-odd. He greeted me with that famous dimpled grin — 'you're on 97, you know' — and assured me that we would reach this milestone together. I gave him a few words of encouragement and instructed him to 'run hard between the wickets,' to which he gave his word.

I crunched the first ball of that over on the up. The sound of bat on ball was so pure, so clean and honest, that I called 'YES' without a moment's hesitation. True to his word, Lloydy ran hard, blindly, without realising that the ball was traveling to conventional mid-off. He wasn't smart, Lloydy. By the time I had the chance to reverse my call it was too late. Lloydy was out for a diamond duck, and suddenly we were 7-200.

The fielding team erupted. 'Well done, champ!' one fielder unctuously sneered. Speechless, I looked back at him blankly. *What have I done?*

The new batsman made his way to the wicket. Chooka: our captain, our guiding light. 'Let's welcome the captain to the crease, lads,' their opposition skipper instructed his teammates, prompting a smattering of polite applause. It'd been years since I'd played in fourths and I'd forgotten about this quaint custom, which sadly, only exists in the lower grades these days. It was a nice gesture, and duly acknowledged by the man himself, in the form of an understated nod. *Cheers, boys.*

Chooka had a round body. His face was puffy and red, likely due to a casual drinking problem. Nonetheless, Chooka had presence. I dearly wanted to gain the respect of Chooka. As he approached, I put my fist out, hoping that Chooka would respond with a glove punch. It was an ugly Americanism that had first crept into the game in the late 1990s, but had since been adopted by the masses, particularly at lower grade and junior level. To my delight, Chooka looked me in the eye and punched my glove with gusto.

'I'll get you there, mate,' he vowed, before waddling back to the non-striker's end.

All was not lost, yet. But now, I had to switch the fuck on. I needed to put the past calamities out of mind. To forget that I'd just run two blokes out in my selfish quest for glory. The collateral damage was huge — we'd gone from coasting at 5-200 to a nervy 7-200 in the space of two minutes; I may have destroyed any chance I had of working at Darryl's listed IT company, or becoming friends with Lloydy. But with the calm, mature influence of Chooka, I could do it.

Three runs. Three runs and you're a hero ...

As I got into position to face the bowler, I could hear the calls from the cordon. 'Team hat-trick lads!' A bat-pad fielder was moved in to position, as if being on a team hat trick was the reason for my nervousness. Seriously, is there anything less exciting than the prospect of a team hat trick? The only people who care about a team hat trick are those who have never achieved personal success. They are the ones who need this, the ones who need, desperately, to feel 'something'. I managed to see the team hat trick ball out, much to the disappointment of the opposition. However, the *real* job was not yet completed. My hundred, still tantalisingly out of reach.

Finally, it presented itself. The opening bowler, now tiring slightly, drifted onto my pads. It was an area, if I may so, that I generally excelled in, chiefly due to my obsession with Mark Waugh as a junior. Waugh, the consummate exponent of the leg glance. I must have practiced his signature shot 10,000 times at home, against the wall. I'd visualised this very moment 10,000 times. Sure, in these backyard fantasies I was usually playing in a test match against the West Indies — as opposed to a meaningless fourth grade fixture in desolate suburbia — but this time it was real. And I was prepared. With sub-continental wrist work, I flicked the ball in front of square, wrong footing the square leg fieldsman, and away it went, making a gratifying thud as it cannoned into the pickets.

The first sound I heard was Nuggsy. 'YIEEEWWWWWWW!' he shrieked. 'HUNDREDDDD!!!!'

The rest of my teammates joined in, even the ones who I'd recently run out, rising from their Ikea seats to applaud in unison. I turned to salute the pavilion, just like I'd always practiced, hands aloft like Nixon, savouring my personal victory. Swept up in the euphoria of it all, I took off my helmet and kissed the badge. Fourth grade: where blokes celebrate tons by kissing a helmet they bought at Rebel Sports. Only I didn't care. I glanced over to the hill. I saw Finn and Lara clapping wildly. I raised both arms again, helmet and bat, to acknowledge them. I was glad they were there.

But where is Dad?

I looked around the ground to see where this mystery man was. Had it all been a mirage? Had I manifested his image there, on the hill? Had Nuggsy been wrong? Perhaps that bloke on the hill was just some random bloke, one of the many strange men that tend to loiter around cricket fields at all hours of the day. I looked all around the ground, desperately hoping he'd seen it, but I couldn't find him. I surmised that he'd probably gone home after I ran Lloydy out, disappointed in me, yet again. Just as I was about to give up, I noticed a strange man near the sightscreen. *It was Dad.* In my blinkered attempt to get to the 100, I'd failed to realise that he had silently made his way up behind the wicket. This was what he used to do when I was a kid: stand behind the bowler in order to get a good view (so he could critique me when I eventually got out). Now, he was there, and I had just hit 100. One hundred runs — all of them mine. I looked at him, waiting for some kind of emotion, an acknowledgement of some kind. It came, eventually, and it was typically understated. A gentle nod and a singular clap, the sound piercing its way through the cold March air and into my eager ears. *Well done, son.* I returned the gesture: a demure bat tip and a quiet nod. *Thanks, Dad.* Gruff masculinity personified. It was the best I'd ever get from Dad — and it was worth the wait.

Fuck, I felt good. I felt alive.

Chooka came down the wicket to give the customary handshake. For once, I nailed it. My hand went in hard and good, meeting his at the perfect pressure point. To my delight, Chooka brought it in for a hug. *Shit, a hug!* The male body contact felt great — it always did. But this time, it was *my* glory to share. I wasn't simply hugging someone else; *I* was being hugged. I had earned this hug.

'Keep going mate. Job's not over,' Chooka advised.

It felt like minutes had passed, but it had only been perhaps 30 seconds since I'd struck the boundary that brought up my ton. Once the commotion had died down, I realised that there was still a game of cricket to be played. *Still a job to be done.*

In the six overs that remained, I entered a trance-like state. I was dominating the attack in a way that I hadn't done since high school. I finished unbeaten on 134, out of a total of 256, walking off the field to a warm reception: the sound of 20 or so people clapping sporadically. A century *and* red ink — is there anything better in life than that? Well, possibly a century/circuit/chop combo, but there was plenty of time for that later. Perhaps Lara and I could go out for dinner and a movie, followed by a night of lovemaking. Sure, it wasn't the archetypal 'triple C' — a glorious hundred + loose circuit with the boys + meaningless one-night stand with an equally lonely woman at 4am — but it was something. It was *something.*

We strode onto the field following the lunch break brimming with optimism and confidence — probably more so than our total of 256 warranted. Chooka had provided us with another fascinating pre-innings speech — this time, focusing on the themes of individualism vs. collectivism, using Ayn Rand's *The Fountainhead* as a reference point — and to a man, we were revved up and ready to go. The team 'energy' was at an unprecedented level, and I, the centurion, was leading the charge. In the early overs, I was a man possessed: dolling out unsolicited bum taps to anyone within reach; urging our bowlers to work hard; demanding we all be 'on our toes' lest an opportunity presented itself. I was absolutely insufferable, a total fucking menace. It had been years since I'd been so fired up on a cricket field. It had only taken an unbeaten hundred to shake me from my decade-long malaise.

Aaron, the young country kid, had been given the new ball, and he didn't disappoint, snaring two early wickets to leave the opposition reeling at 2-5 after three overs. Jordie looked equally likely to cause trouble, but was only allowed to bowl five overs due to age restrictions, and went wicket-less. After the early collapse, our opposition fought back to be about 2-60 at drinks, leaving the game evenly poised on a pretty flat deck.

We needed a breakthrough. Soon after drinks, Chooka gestured over to me to limber up, indicating that I'd have the next over. This was my chance to back up my batting performance. I gave Chooka a quick nod and went through the typical warm-up stretches, loosening my shoulder and back for battle. I hadn't bowled all season, but this was fourth grade — and here, it seemed I was king of the village. I was like one of those blokes in African countries who have 45 wives, just taking what I wanted at will. A big fish in a small pond; just the way I liked it.

As I stood at the top of my mark, Chooka came over to me from his position at mid-off, put a fatherly hand on my shoulder, and talked through the areas in which I should be focusing on: full and straight. I was always an aggressive bowler, despite my rapidly declining pace, so at the back of my mind existed the ever-present urge to bounce my opponent. It was an urge I had tried to resist in recent years, but for the sake of the team, I resolved to heed Chooka's advice.

Full and straight. No dramas, mate.

Just as I was about to run in for my first delivery, I noticed — to my horror — our keeper, Smithy, was standing up to me. There is no greater alpha showdown than that between the arrogant keeper and the seamer whose bowling he has deemed slow enough to stand up to. It's basically an attack on your manhood. Smithy was a lovely bloke with a winning smile and a great attitude, but at this moment he was dead to me.

Fuck that. I don't care if Chooka set a 7-2 field. I'm going to lid this bloke.

I sprinted to the crease and hurled myself towards the batsman, a veritable blur of arms, legs and chest. But in that infinitesimal moment between gather and release, I swiftly calculated that I wouldn't have the pace to bounce my wicketkeeper. The ball would likely bounce up at chest height, having slowed dramatically off the wicket, and present the batsman with an easy pull shot to the fence. As such, I resolved to do the unthinkable: to bowl a beamer.

Bowling a beamer is basically the loosest, most subversive thing you can do on a cricket field. There is nothing more frowned upon in all of cricket, really, aside from the 'Mankad'. But while I was enjoying my new surroundings, my immediate success, I was still undeniably a grade cricketer. You can take the boy out of grade cricket, but you can't take grade cricket out of the boy. Having spent years surrounded by utter fuckwits, I, too, had become a fuckwit. I was a product of my environment.

The ball shot out of my hand at head height, causing the batsman to scurry out of the way, muttering a few choice words. But I wasn't concerned with his reaction. My focus was on Smithy.

'Still want to stand up to me, champ?' I snarled.

'Shit, sorry mate. I thought you were bowling leg spin,' was his genuine reply.

Once again, the response drew laughter from all around the wicket. To be fair, my run up was only eight paces — so I could understand the confusion. I wasn't a noted bowler, so how could Smithy have known what to expect? On Tuesday night at training, I'd been imitating the 1990's South African left-arm leg-spinner Paul Adams — best known for his 'frog in a blender' action — in the third net for a laugh. Still, it was yet another chastening humiliation in a career littered by them. I made a feeble attempt to backtrack — 'sorry mate, was only kidding … it slipped out!' — but it did nothing to curb the laughter. This kind of misguided alpha aggression wouldn't fly in the convivial confines of fourth grade. I had to rid myself of this defensive reflex.

I got through the rest of my over without further incident, although perhaps unsurprisingly, it was to be my only one for the innings. And despite my strident efforts in the field, we were unable to halt the opposition's run chase. They ended up passing our total with seven overs to spare.

We had lost the final game of the season.

I always hated the moments directly after a loss, where we'd sit in our dressing room and listen to the opposition sing their club song, enjoying the spoils of victory, arms linked, swilling beers like Freemasons. The throaty growls of 11 tuneless men singing a song penned by alcoholic ex-players that usually didn't even rhyme. Of course, the team song was strictly reserved for the rare occasions we got a win. The whole reason for singing it was to make the opposition hear it, to rub in the loss. It didn't seem right. I'd hit a hundred, we'd had a good day out, but now, we had to sit there and listen to this.

A passion stirred within me. I had forgotten what it was like to come so close and yet so far. I'd hit a hundred, put in all my effort, but we'd still lost. Suddenly, I felt myself rise to my feet.

'Lads, if I could just get a bit of quiet for moment, I've got something I'd like to say.'

A hush came over the dressing room. The floor was mine. I took a deep breath and spoke from the heart.

'Normally, I feel a great sense of relief after the final game of the season, in that I don't have to see these terrible blokes I play with for another six months.'

A few half-laughs broke out. I pressed on with my soliloquy.

'I'm 29 years of age in a couple of weeks. I've been playing cricket for about two decades. I was the best player in my age group all the way through, but things changed when I got to grade cricket. I struggled to find my place within the strict social hierarchy. It stopped being fun. But today, I've had a great time playing with you blokes. And for the first time in years, I scored some runs, too. I felt good out there. I felt confident. It *was* fun. And when I hear that fucking team song in there, those blokes screaming their hearts out, it pisses me off that we don't have anything to sing in here, regardless of the result.'

I knew the next thing I had to say would cause a stir, but I went for it anyway.

'Lads, I know that this might sound a bit *rare*, but I'd like to read a few lines from a poem, if I may.'

I'd been reading poetry at book club — Edgar Allen Poe, Walt Whitman, Emily Dickinson, and several other notable nineteenth century American laureates. I heard a couple of murmurs among the playing group — *what's this bloke up to?* — but blocked it all out. I cleared my throat, closed my eyes, and hoped for the best.

'Success is counted sweetest
By those who ne'er succeed.

To comprehend a nectar
Requires sorest need.

Not one of all the purple Host
Who took the Flag today
Can tell the definition
So clear of victory

As he defeated — dying —
On whose forbidden ear
The distant strains of triumph
Burst agonised and clear!'

I thought the poem was well chosen. It would remind the players that we, in losing, are now better prepared to understand victory. That the 'distant strains of triumph' — in this case, the opposition's team song — would teach us the true value of winning. That victory and defeat are both equally fleeting in nature.

To my distress, two or three seconds passed without anyone saying a word.

Shit, you've outdone yourself this time. Grade cricket isn't ready for Emily Dickinson.

Then, to my relief, a slow clap emanated from the shadowy, mildewed corner of the dressing room. Nuggsy's corner. As always, Nuggsy was in my corner.

'Mate, that's one of the best things I've ever heard. Fucking emotional. Every time we lose from now on, we'll recite that as a team, together. Who'd you say it was by — Emma Dickens?'

'Emily Dickinson. One of the greatest American poets of all time, Nuglet.'

'Well bloody oath, that got to me,' Nuggsy said, wiping away a tear.

Chooka winked at me as he rose purposefully from his bench. 'Lads, I want you all to learn that poem over the off-season,' he announced. 'Hopefully we won't have to recite it too many times next year, but that's a bloody good idea. A team losing song, to inspire us to future victories!'

And there it was. I had made my mark on grade cricket. I had scored a century and I was the founding father of a new, obscure concept: the team losing song. Whenever our team lost from now on, we would recite Emily Dickinson's famous poem, like soldiers mourning a lost battle. I'm not sure if there is anything more incongruous than maudlin, Victorian-era poetry addressed to a group of amateur Australian cricketers following a loss, but I didn't care. There we stood, defeated, weary, in various states of undress. At that moment, we were more than just a cricket team made up of 11 blokes from disparate backgrounds. We were together. We were a unit.

Just a few games prior, when at my lowest point, I had resolved to quit after the final game. However, that decision had now been complicated by my unlikely century in the final game of the season. Did I want to go out on top, like Joe DiMaggio, hanging up the cleats after a World Series win? Or would I wait too long, like Muhammad Ali, and bow out bloated, beaten, and suffering from a thyroid condition?

I sidled over to Chooka, who was sitting in the corner nursing a can of VB. 'Chooka, mate. Have you ever considered giving the game away?'

Chooka relaxed his shoulders, took a generous swig of his VB, and stared out the dressing room window, contemplatively. 'Yes, mate. Several times, actually. Especially when I was around your age — in and out of the grades, searching for meaning in my cricket.'

'And what changed?'

Chooka shrugged, took another sip. 'Mate, eventually I just became comfortable with myself. You seem like a bright kid — and someone who loves cricket. Let me just say that if you really love the game of cricket, that should be enough. Don't worry about moving up and down the grades, son. Don't worry about your rig. When I finally let go of all these insecurities — my batting average, my rig, circuiting — that's when I could finally relax and enjoy the game again, just like I did as a kid.'

Chooka's words rang true. I did still love cricket. Today was evidence of that. Perhaps it *was* time to stop worrying about what other cricketers thought of me. To go back to the days when I was young; where I didn't even think twice about my social standing within a club, or whether my penis was big enough to garner begrudging respect in the dressing rooms.

'Chooka, do you remember that time when you came into the bar with Vikram and a couple of the other fourth graders, and Marty Henson called you a paedophile for basically no reason?' I began, tentatively.

'Ah yeah, I remember that.'

'Well … I felt really bad that I didn't stick up for you. I still do, actually. I was just trying to fit in.'

'Look mate, it's nothing. Have you ever heard the expression, "*champ or be …*"'

'*Champed!*' I butted in. 'Yes, I have heard that phrase. But to be honest, I lived by that creed for most of my playing career. Are you saying that this is a flawed philosophy?'

'Absolutely, mate. Don't worry. One day, as I said, these sorts of things won't bother you any more. It seems significant right now, but in the grand scheme of things, it means absolutely nothing.'

I now understood why the older blokes couldn't give the game away. I no longer felt sorry for those men who spent their weekends battling away in park cricket, a shadow of their former selves. When played in the right spirit, with the right group of blokes, cricket *was* fun. It was how it started out — and perhaps, this was how it would end. My middling middle years would go down in history as a mere aberration, bookended by brilliance. All I really wanted was to compete with my mates on Saturday and hit a few runs in the process. At the end of the day, we'd have a few beers, regardless of the result. We'd have a shower. We'd have a sing. Maybe we'd have a circuit. They say the true definition of insanity is repeating the same thing over and over again, but still expecting a different result. It's a tired cliché, but one that had perfectly described my grade cricket experience to this point. Every year, I played cricket. Every year, I averaged between 13.5 and 18. But this century was a true outlier. Maybe I wasn't so insane? Maybe Einstein was wrong, after all?

As I made my way out of the dressing room, heavy kit slung over my shoulder, I saw Dad chatting amicably with Lara and Finn, arms crossed, beer in hand. On closer inspection, he was smiling. *My Dad was smiling!* The mere sight left me with a slight dizziness, as if I'd just given blood. I wondered whether he'd let me sit in the front seat on the way home. We'd pull in to McDonald's Drive Thru; I'd order a Big Mac meal, he'd tell me not to spill any of it on the leather seats. We'd drive home, in silence, radio tuned to the soft, analogue sounds of ABC *Grandstand*, just like old times. I sighed at the thought.

Should I ask him? I could always come back and pick my car up later ...

Fuck it. Maybe I will go around again next season.

GLOSSARY

Alpha (n): 1. The dominant male among a specific group of males, often the strongest and most physically intimidating. *'Nuggsy's a fucking alpha dog.'* **2. (v)** To employ aggressive masculinity in one's body/voice in order to dominate someone else. *'Their skipper alpha'd me at the coin toss.'*

Baker's whites (n): Cheap, brightly coloured cricket attire, usually purchased at an all-sports retail chain as opposed to a dedicated cricket warehouse. *'Robbo's wearing baker's whites again — he must have bought those at Rebel Sports.'*

Beamer (n): A full toss aimed at the batsman's head, intentionally or otherwise.

Bodyline (n): A controversial tactic deployed by the English Cricket Team in the early 1930s in order to combat Don Bradman's Australia. It involved bowling at the batsman's body and placing close fielders around the batsman on the leg-side.

Bud (n): Slang for 'friend'. Has genial connotations. *'Cheers, bud.'*

Burglar (n): Someone who has gotten away with a particularly audacious or improbable act on (or off) the cricket field. *'Timbo burgled that catch! The burglar!'*

Champ (n): Slang for friend. Often used pejoratively when looking to subvert a lesser player. *'Yeah good one, champ.'*

Champed (v): The act of calling one 'champ'. *'Dazza champed me at training the other day.'*

Chat (n): The level of wit one displays both on and off the cricket field. *'John's a nice enough bloke but he's got shit chat.'*

Chop (n): Sexual intercourse. *'Nuggsy burgled a chop last night. Gesture!'*

Chop King (n): The player with the most impressive (recent) sexual history.

Chub up (v): The act of tapping one's genitals to increase blood flow to give the (false) impression of a large manhood. *'It's obviously important to chub up before stepping in the team showers.'*

Circuit (n): The specific set of bars or pubs that a group of people choose to frequent on a regular basis. *'Crows Town has a pretty good circuit.'*

Clicks (adj): The descriptor for how fast one bowls, usually a reference to km/h. *'Dazza's rapid — he bowls 130 clicks.'*

Coat (n): An acronym for 'cunt of a thing', a widely used insult in grade cricket circles, particularly in the early 2000s. *'Robbo is an absolute coat.'*

Cordon (n): The collective group of fielders standing behind the batsman in catching positions on the off side. *'I hope I can snag a spot in the cordon this season.'*

Creams (n): Proper cricket attire, generally off-white in colour. *'Fuck Damo looks good in creams.'*

Dot ball (n): A delivery bowled whereupon no runs are conceded.

Drinks (n): A break in play, generally taken on the hour, where drinks are brought out onto the field for the players and umpires. The drink of choice is generally a mix of concentrated cordial and water (see: 'good ratios').

Forward defence (n): A defensive stroke wherein the batsman steps forward to a delivery and plays it directly into the ground.

French Cricket (n): A social game, often played at picnics, whereby one batsman must survive against a group of fielders/bowlers for as long as possible. There are just two modes of dismissal: caught and hit on the leg below the knee.

Gesture (adj): A word used to describe a positive, yet unexpected outcome. *'Got a win with my first tap on the pokies tonight. Gesture!'*

Golden Triangle (n): A series of (usually three) drinking establishments frequented after a day's play. This will generally include the closest pub to the home ground followed by two shadier venues once the beers are flowing. *'Nuggsy got lost in the golden triangle last weekend looking for a chop. Great circuit, though.'*

Good ratios (adj): A stock phrase used to describe the ratio of concentrated cordial mix to water during the drinks break.

Great man (n): A commonly used term of endearment. Can be used earnestly or pejoratively, depending on the context. *'Here he is — it's the great man!'*

Incrediball (n): A replica cricket ball designed for junior cricketers. The soft polyurethane core is less likely to cause injury.

Leg-side (n): The area of the field to the left of a right-handed batsman and to right of a left-handed batman.

Levers (n): Long arms. One blessed with 'levers' may have a natural advantage over his peers when it comes to throwing further, bowling faster and hitting longer.

Lid (n): 1. A cricket helmet. **2. (n)** One's head of hair.

Lip (n): A colloquial term for 'sledging' (see below). *'Those pricks gave some serious lip out there.'*

Mankad (n): A controversial (yet legitimate) form of dismissal, where the bowler runs the non-striker out before entering his delivery stride. Sometimes used as a last resort by struggling fielding sides.

Map (n): A loose, misogynistic term for 'woman'. Has its origin in the colloquial phrase 'Map of Tasmania' — a reference to the shape of a woman's pubic mound. *'Nuggsy's chopped three maps this year and counting. Result!'*

Meat (n): The thickest, most powerful area of a cricket bat.

MyCricket (n): An online portal and mobile application that contains up-to-date information on all cricket fixtures, scorecards, ladders, player stats.

Nets (n): A cricket pitch or series of pitches surrounded by netting — the typical setting for cricket practice.

Off-side (n): The area of the field to the right of a right-handed batsman and to left of a left-handed batman.

Old mate (n): Slang for person, can be used in both positive and negative situations.

Optic (v): To see. *'You can get a good optic from here.'*

Pill (n): A cricket ball.

Pipes (n): Well-developed arms, generally the result of extensive resistance training. *'I train chest and pipes on Tuesdays and Thursdays.'*

Poles (n): Dismissals, wickets taken by a bowler. *'Jordie snared three poles and was unlucky not to pick up a fourth.'*

Rare (adj): A (negative) term used to describe someone who is naturally 'different', or simply refuses to adhere to expected societal norms. It is thought to derive from the Latin phrase *rara avis*, meaning 'rare bird'. *'Chooka's a rare unit. I hear he reads poetry in his spare time.'*

Red ink (n): A not out batsman. Scorers will record an undefeated innings using red ink. A player who regularly records 'red ink' scores may acquire a higher batting average than his peers, since batting averages are calculated as runs divided by outs. *'Damo loves the red ink — he's averaging 42 this season.'*

Result (n): Term used to convey delight upon securing a desired circumstance or set of circumstances. *'I was drinking with Bruiser, who made commission this month, and was desperate to throw his cash around. Result!'*

Rig (n): Another term for one's body, applicable to both males and females. *'Bretty had a great technique and a great rig: he was the complete cricketer.'*

Shires (n): A Sydney Cricket competition that sits separate to grade cricket, and generally deemed to be of a lower standard. Despite all this, Shires clubs sometimes pay more than grade clubs. *'I've had enough of grade cricket. Think I might play Shires next year: Lindfield's offering me a package.'*

Skins (n): Tights for your legs or torso to give the appearance of athleticism, though anyone who wears them will describe them as compression garments.

Sledging (v): Verbal intimidation or insults designed to gain psychological ascendance over another player or break their concentration.

Spikes (n): Sharp, usually metallic studs affixed to the sole of a cricket boot to aid stability in the field.

Spirit of Cricket (n): An initiative launched by Cricket Australia some years ago whereby umpires award points to each team based on their conduct, including language, sportsmanship and attitude towards umpires.

Stick (n): A cricket bat.

Stretching circle (n): A seated circle formed by all teams in the pre-match warm up — officially convened for the purposes of stretching muscles, though its primary purpose is to provide a democratic forum for the exchange of sex tales.

T-Drill (n): A training exercise designed to improve multiple elements of ground fielding. Widely employed across all clubs as an easy way to get everyone doing something. Looks vaguely professional.

Tea (n): An officially sanctioned break in play reserved for the afternoon. Traditionally, the home team will be called upon to provide snacks for the consumption of all and the judgment of the away team. No one can ever remember if this break goes for twenty or thirty minutes.

Throwdowns (v): A common warm up drill for batsmen that involves a ball thrown to the batsman, preferably directed toward the optimal area for said batsman to strike the ball forcefully. *'Give us some throwdowns, champ, I'm batting three today.'*

Two legs (n): A batting position in which the batsman aligns his stance with the gap between middle and leg stump. *'Bradman took a 'two leg' guard at the crease, so I will too.'*

Village (adj): A pejorative term that describes a particularly amateurish effort by an individual or the team at large — usually in regards to style. While its origin stems specifically from the substandard village competition throughout England and Wales, the term is nonetheless universal. *'Did you see that Timbo wore his thigh pad on the outside of his trousers? Fucking village.'*

Work hard (v): A phrase typically bellowed from one teammate to another under the guise of encouragement, but can also be used as thinly veiled criticism towards someone who has made a mistake. Can also reveal a decidedly limited vocabulary. *'We're defending 110 so we're going to have to work hard!'*

Yiew (n): A joyous cry upon a favourable moment in a game, training or social situation. Employed more so by individuals and teams hailing from low socioeconomic regions. *'I tonned up today Mum. Yiew!'*

Yuck (n): Term employed to indicate deep disgust at another's behaviour or appearance. *'Have a go at this bloke's rig. Yuck.'*

9 781922 129581

Printed in February 2021
by Rotomail Italia S.p.A., Vignate (MI) - Italy